This book describes life as an apprentice in the 1950s in one of England's biggest electrical companies, and is presented through the eyes of an apprentice whose experiences are those of the author and other contemporary contributors.

"Well done, the book is very amusing and fully captures the conditions as an apprentice in my time. Not a lot seems to have changed over the years?"
(Prof. Sterling, retd. Vice Chancellor, Birmingham University)

"Very enjoyable. A true picture of the shop floor. It's all there except the smell!"
(Colin Adams, retd. Managing Director, specialist heavy machining company)

"A fascinating insight into the life as an apprentice in the 1950s. The shop floor banter was humorous and the camaraderie between the workers was apparent. An enjoyable read for anyone of any age!"
(Ed Weston, student, Hartpury College Gloucester)

"Foolish happy days. I never minded coming back off holidays"
(Ex-apprentice letter)

ACKNOWLEDGEMENTS

Grateful thanks are due to the many neighbours, family, and ex–GEC Apes who have contributed in so many ways to the contents. Their range of reminiscences, general encouragement, corrections and invaluable advice, have made the writing of this book a great source of education and pleasure. Also many thanks to Kevin Pocock for permission to include his painting of Poole Harbour (Chpt. 10).

Ken Parton
November 2011

TALES FROM THE TOOL BOX

LIFE AS A *GEC* APPRENTICE

KEN PARTON

Matador
9 Priory Business Park
Kibworth Beauchamp
Leicestershire LE8 0RX, UK
Tel: (+44) 116 279 2299
Fax: (+44) 116 279 2277
Email: books@troubador.co.uk
Web: www.troubador.co.uk/matador

ISBN 978 1780884 356

British Library Cataloguing in Publication Data.
A catalogue record for this book is available from the British Library.

Typeset in 11pt Bembo by Troubador Publishing Ltd, Leicester, UK
Printed and bound in the UK by TJ International, Padstow, Cornwall

Matador is an imprint of Troubador Publishing Ltd

CONTENTS

(Cartoons resurrected from the GEC Witton Apprentices Association
Journals 1951–1956) © Ken Parton

LIST OF ILLUSTRATIONS

★ Artist, Kevin. J. Pocock, email k@kjpocock.com

LIST OF CARTOONS

CHAPTER 1

"Clocking in"

Starting work in a big city after growing up in the country was probably not going to be that easy thought Roger, as he dismounted his rather battered bike and entered the apprentice's hall of residence. It was only a few years after the Second World War and Roger, fresh from college, had just cycled his way from Birmingham New Street station to this palatial hall where he would be spending the next two years. He was immediately impressed. The building, Castle Bromwich Hall, was a large mansion, built, he was to learn in about 1580 and considered a Jacobean masterpiece. It still retained all its original features including a large expanse of garden. The grandeur of the place took his breath away as, during the five mile ride from the station, he had been appalled by the scars still evident from the war.

The year was 1951 and there was still a great amount of war-time bomb damage everywhere. Roger thanked his lucky stars that having been brought up in rural Sussex, his life had been pretty cushy until now. Many happy memories flooded back including days on the South Downs with his pals. One of their hobbies had been collecting odd-looking devices left behind from army training exercises, and these "souvenirs" had often given their mothers near heart failure when brought home. "Ah well," he thought coming back to reality, "in for a penny, in for a pound," to quote Shakespeare or somebody, and, dismounting his bike, he unstrapped his saddlebag and strode in through the servants' back door.

Roger had celebrated his 21st birthday that summer and had just completed a two-year, post-war crash course at university in electrical engineering. He had chosen engineering because he was good at maths and he was advised that he would have no trouble getting a job in that profession. At the final exams he only managed a second class honours degree and was told it was his own fault: he would have got a first if he hadn't spent so much time playing cricket for the university, and table tennis where he had a cup to his name. "If only," he thought afterwards but he felt satisfied with his results as he had received three offers of jobs in his last term. He had chosen this one which entailed a two-year, full-time heavy engineering apprenticeship at the General Electric Company in Witton. During the job interviews he had expressed an interest in becoming a design engineer and this offer was the only one that demanded an honours degree. So, with his exam results, it seemed the obvious one to choose. This journey to the Midlands was also the first time that Roger had ever been north of London, and Sussex already seemed far away. Now, in every sense of the word, he was feeling very much a new boy. Roger quite expected the change of life-style to be pretty awful. As it turned out, however, he would spend twenty-one years in this first job and look back at that time with nothing but warm nostalgia. The time would turn out to be some of the best years of his life, full of incident, learning, shared skills, companionship and often quite hilarious humour.

There were some fifty company apprentices staying at the Hall and Roger found himself being taken for granted straight away

Well I don't exacty… errr… own it!

without any formalities. He was shown his bedroom, an elegant oak-panelled room, sharing with three other graduates, none of whom had yet returned from their weekends away. Roger felt at home immediately because the room was far from tidy! Roger was given a few sandwiches as he was too late for Hall dinner and he munched them in silence in the common room. This room had once been the hall drawing room. It was a long, spacious room with a high ceiling and he felt dwarfed by three enormous tapestries on the walls. He was told they had hung there for well over a hundred years. Roger finished his sandwiches, returned to the bedroom, spent a short time unpacking his few belongings and retired gratefully to bed. He felt physically and emotionally drained.

The next morning, his very first day, Roger began with a pretty decent breakfast among some fifty rapacious apprentices and very nice it was too. Rationing was still strict in the outside world, but here he had the choice of starters, followed by eggs, bacon, sausage and sauté potatoes. There was even bubble and squeak, one of his wartime favourites at home. As he tucked in, he soon realised that those around him were gobbling food down at great speed in order to catch the works bus which was waiting patiently outside the door. This bus would take them off to the factory some six miles away in the heart of the city and among the many obvious new recruits Roger could detect a rather apprehensive atmosphere, halfway between going to a dentist and attending a funeral.

Roger was not going on the free bus. He had his trusted pushbike from home to which he was very much attached and he valued his independence. The bike itself had seen much better days, and while still at school there had been a spot police inspection of bicycles one day because of the number of accidents being caused by unfit machines. Roger had just heard of this in time and had rescued his bike from the cycle racks and hidden it in the school air raid shelters. It had rather rudimentary brakes, a battered frame, no front mudguard and no lights. He guessed he might have been in trouble. One of these days, he told himself, he would buy a new machine but he would wear this old one out first.

Roger had only a vague idea how to get to work that first day but coming up from the country, where everything was straightforward, he was sure he could trust his sense of direction. He spotted several other established residents who were just mounting their bikes and asked them if they would just set him off in the right direction. "Sure," said the pack leader, "come with us, but it's a bit tricky," and casting a sorrowful eye on Roger's bike he added "that is, if you can keep up!"

"What an insult" thought Roger to himself, "just you wait and see."

"Have you ever ridden over tram lines?" the pack leader asked as they all mounted, "because it's a wet morning and you have to be bit careful." Now Roger had only met tram lines for the first time the day before on his way from the station to the Hall, and had identified them as a potential death trap. They were two strips of steel flush to the road surface and running for miles all over the city with a neat gap between them that exactly fitted a bicycle front wheel. If your wheel slipped into one, the only way out was over the handle bars which took about two seconds. This would be particularly awkward if you had just nipped in front of a trundling tram.

"Oh sure," he answered, for he was fond of his own bike and prided himself on his skill and fitness. After all, wasn't he the only one at home who had completed a circuit of the village green with five up on the bike? One sitting on the handlebars, one on his shoulders, one on the saddle, with Roger himself standing up on the pedals, and one standing on the back axle nuts clinging on to the man in front. A sixth cautious individual had tried to mount on what was left of the crossbar, but immediate pains in his lower anatomy made him jump off even before they started. They had all been fifth form schoolboys back then, but you had to make your own fun in the country. As for keeping up with his fellow apprentices, he had no fears on that score either. Hadn't he often come first in the local dirt track bike races? Plus, having just come up from a summer on the farm, he felt supremely fit. He thought many of those around him looked rather pale and grey in comparison.

So, on that damp and cheerless morning, off they went into the city tearing along the six miles to the works, weaving in and out of traffic, puffing away, and making short work of a rather tedious journey. Roger kept up with the pack with no trouble and negotiated the tramlines with a flare that won him some silent admiration. There was a general sharp ringing of bicycle bells, except from Roger. He had never needed one at home but he was now finding that the rattling of his loose rear wheel mudguard made a useful alternative. Not only did Roger have no trouble in keeping up but if he had known the way, he would have sprinted ahead at the end just to show them there was nothing wrong with him — or his bike.

The last hundred yards of the run were tricky as the route finished along the canal towpath which at that time of day was crowded with people on their way to work. The only way through for a bike was along the edge near the grimy water and on a wet day, with the towpath edged with large uneven flagstones, the trudging masses had enough sense to keep a careful distance from the edge. This left just enough room for a bike. Roger lost ground over this part of the run as without a bell he could not warn people he was coming up behind. Erring on the side of caution, he slowed down to the pace of the crowd. Not so the others who, with practice, could judge the next gap to a nicety, ring their bell and shoot past. To be fair, this did not always work, and one celebrated apprentice had recently shot into the water for the third time and held the record. When he was pulled out in a rather dazed condition and taken to the medical centre, all he could remember was being transfixed by the sight of his bike laying at the bottom with its rear red back light still bravely shining up through the green and slimy water. Local wits later assured Roger that no-one had ever drowned in the canal – they had all died of poisoning first!

Eaten any good cyclists lately?

Although the canal path was notorious, Roger soon became adept at the run to work and worked out his own way of getting along the canal path. You had to cycle near the water's edge, of course, but the problem was that when you came up behind a person walking with his back to you, in a hurry and deep in gloomy thoughts, they would not hear you until the last moment. This could well startle them, cause them to jump with a jerk and potentially send you and your bike careering into the water. The strategy Roger therefore adopted was to zoom past without a sound so that the pedestrian only jumped after you had shot past. In time he developed this to a fine art, sometimes getting past with nearly half a tyre over the edge. Cyclists were very unpopular at that time of the day.

Once he was safely past the works' policeman on the canal gate and had parked his bike, Roger had his first taste of officialdom by having to "clock in". This involved standing in a grey queue, selecting your own "clock card" from a rack and shuffling forward until at last you came to a pretty battered old machine that had seen better days. This device, indispensable to management, had a clock facing you and a slot at the front into which you entered your card. You then pulled the handle down, like a one-armed bandit and with a large ping of a bell, the machine stamped the time on to your card which you then stacked back in the rack. Sometimes there came the sound of five or six pings in very rapid succession which would cause a little man in an office to pop out and check it wasn't an apprentice with a fistful of cards clocking all his mates in. He never caught anybody. Another problem Roger discovered in time was the habit of many apprentices of turning up at the very last second before start time.

Clocking in!

This often caused an unholy scramble with everyone trying to "clock in" at once. It was really much easier to get a pal who was regularly early — and there were a few, to clock in for you.

Roger now found himself being ushered into the holy of holies, the Education and Training Office, or the ETO as it was known. This collection of huts was the hub of all apprentice activities and became a sort of Mecca for anyone in trouble, dissatisfied, bored, or really for anyone who just wanted a quiet break from whatever they were supposed to be doing. It was always busy. Roger and all the newcomers were ushered into a room for their first initiation,

"Good Morning lads," said a kind looking gentleman, "My name is Jim Hudson and I have pleasure in welcoming you to Witton. I am the second in command to the Education and Training Officer, Mr Rollason and I am responsible for organising your training plan. For graduate apprentices this is a two-year course as you know and for student apprentices, the course is for five years. Not that they are slower on the uptake" he paused for a smile, "but they have a lot of study still to do to reach the necessary academic standards to become a qualified engineer."

He stopped to let this significant gem sink in. He then continued, "For the majority of your time you will be working on the shop floor, including a stint in the foundry, so it is important that you have good sensible overalls and especially importantly, have good strong shoes. We strongly advise you to purchase a pair of "toe-tectors" which look like a strong shoe or boot but have an inbuilt steel toecap. Once you have had someone drop a steel bar across your toes, you will appreciate their advantages." Roger felt really at home with this advice. Having worked on the land in all weathers he well knew the value of strong footwear and he studied some of new recruits' thin papery shoes with a certain feeling of smugness. Mr Hudson continued, "You can purchase 'toe-tectors' in the works canteen shop and you will be surprised at how cheap they are. They are government supported and, funnily enough, quite comfortable to wear. Well," he said with a smile, "that's the only commercial you will get from me," and he proceeded to roll out a large map of the works in front of them.

"Inside this factory complex," he said, "we make everything electrical right from torch batteries up to the largest electric motors and power system generators in the world. We have customers all over the world and, now that the war is over, we are almost overwhelmed with orders and demands for our technical skills. To cope with this demand, especially with the rapidly moving technical advances in our industry, we need all the skilled and trained manpower that we can get. That's why we have, at present, a total of about seven hundred apprentices on our books, including drawing office, trade, student and graduate, all at different stages of their courses."

"With the help of this map," continued our learned guide, "I will now give you a quick run-down of where everything is situated on the site. First I must apologise for this slightly shabby building we are in!"

"You can say that again", thought Roger for they were in a rather battered hut, surrounded by a few other wartime huts looking even worse for wear.

"Still, don't worry," beamed our indefatigable tutor, "we have plans over the next few years to build a splendid new large turbo-alternator hall, with smart offices included, some of which will be for us."

As Roger, like most of those present had no idea what to expect, this promise of a future heaven, clearly a significant dream in Mr Hudson's eyes, left them all distinctly unimpressed.

"Now," continued our tutor happily, "we have down this side of the main drive the switchgear factory and the transformer shop. By switchgear, I don't mean the little switches on your wall at home, but real switches for factory supplies and up to mighty big circuit breakers in power stations coping with voltages of more than 100,000 volts and many thousands of amps. When power stations were developing, switching off large electric currents was sometimes very difficult. Many engineers tell that in earlier power stations they used to have large crude switches some six feet tall along one wall, consisting of a copper blade, hinged near the floor and slotting into a sliding connection at the top. You opened the switch by standing back and holding a large wooden pole with a hook on the end, you pulled the blade smartly out of the top connection and let it swing down and crash to the floor. Sometimes the current passing was so high that it didn't go out but carried on as a long glowing arc down the wall with enough noise to frighten the very devil himself. The engineer would be ready for this and hastily fan the arc out with a large fan always kept there for such contingencies." "Nowadays," Mr Hudson said smiling at us, "we can do much better than that of course, and all big circuit breakers are mounted inside steel tanks with automatic devices to snuff out any arc on the very first cycle of the alternating current. However," he continued beaming, "we still have to regularly test new designs and we have a switchgear testing station over here," he said pointing to his map, "far away on this hill next to the laboratories. Now and then we have trouble with a new design and you might hear a very big bang as a trial design blows up. As a precaution, this is a protected area, everyone is locked out when testing is going on!"

"Next to the switchgear works," he continued, "there is another laboratory where you may also hear large bangs and crackling noises. This is the high-voltage testing laboratory where all large outdoor high-voltage equipment is subject to the equivalent of a lightning strike before it leaves the factory. Lightning is a funny thing and can cause voltage surges that travel along overhead wires and carry on into the equipment, particularly outdoor transformers and switchgear. We have to design them so that any surges that travel to these units do not cause any internal damage. You will often smell gas ozone around this area when testing is in process." He smiled, "As you know, ozone in small doses is a perfectly harmless gas, there are plenty worse smells you will get used to during your travels." He smiled happily at his own wit while Roger inwardly groaned "How much longer is he going on for?" he thought, as he knew all this already from the brochures he had studied at college.

But nothing was going to deter the cheerful Mr Hudson. "Now here," he beamed "further along, we have the transformer works. Transformers as you know, are needed everywhere to transform one voltage into another. Quite how they work is difficult to explain to a layman so I advise you to keep away from the subject if you are asked by a visitor. You can see small transformers mounted on poles all over the countryside starting with small ones in rural districts feeding small hamlets and isolated houses at the supply of 240 volts, right up to the giants in large electricity substations handling voltages of many thousands. One thing of interest," he added as an afterthought, "you may be interested to know that all transformers have their tank full to the brim with transformer oil — a nasty substance with a very low density. Workers have been known to fall into the tank, which hasn't happened here, thank goodness, but where it has, the worker has sunk straight to the bottom. By the time he has been fished out, perhaps only a matter of thirty seconds or so he is already past recovering."

On this cheery note the new recruits were offered a well needed break. A tea lady had come in with her battered tea trolley, just about supporting an urn that looked as though it had fortified many throughout the war. "And for a good time before then by the looks of if it," thought Roger. At least the tea was hot and as he supped, Roger ruminated about transformers and their use of magnetism. "Interesting," he mused. "We can make atomic bombs, but, like gravity, even Einstein can't explain magnetism."

"We now come to some more dangerous areas", said Mr Hudson after they had re-assembled. "These are the rotating machine shops, starting with the small fractional horsepower single phase motors you find in all sorts of household devices and going right up to enormous three or more thousand horse-power giants. These are built in the 'big shops' which are very dangerous and often noisy places. We ask you to always be very careful on these assignments and not to take any risks or short cuts with jobs you may be asked to do. If you are asked to do something you don't quite understand please ask again – never just think you have understood." He paused to emphasise the word "Never". "The majority of accidents in these areas are caused by apprentices who already think they know it all!" He looked hard at the group and they all squirmed a little in their seats, "There is no place in manufacturing for 'clever clogs' as we would put it."

"As if we would," thought Roger who, like the rest of the

assembly, was a little put out by these remarks. "Wasn't this supposed to be a welcoming introduction? Not a blessed health warning!"

"I won't bore you with any more today," he said, much to the general relief, "except briefly to say," pointing to the map, "the rest of the works goes like this." He indicated one spot after another, "Here, the foundry, here the main test site for large machines, here the Q shop, where the fair sex have a monopoly of workers, here the Mica shop where we handle heat resistant materials. Finally here, the magnet works where during the war we built the magnetic mine-sweeping devices that nullified magnetic mines and saved many ships during the battle of the Atlantic."

Roger was by now feeling rather sleepy, the last few days before he left home had been very hectic and he was now suffering. His mind wandered back to the sunny days in Sussex and the glorious days spent up on the South Downs. On several occasions, he had set off with a pal at six o'clock on a Sunday morning and walked a planned course of fifty miles; getting back home by about seven o'clock in the evening. They used to deliberately challenge themselves to such a test. He smiled remembering the one occasion where they had run out of water and stopped at a remote house to beg a drink. The house turned out to be the local vicarage and the elderly vicar seemed a bit distressed at their semi-exhausted state giving them hot tea and some rock cakes. He said that for all he knew they could be angels in disguise. When they told their pals back home afterwards you could hear the hoots of laughter half a mile away! Roger pulled his mind back to the present with a jerk.

Mr Hudson was still rattling on. He paused for a breath and continued! "Well, next we have here the laboratories where we do testing of new materials and general investigations. Next door, this large area here called MAR, is where we make mercury arc rectifiers. Here is the medical centre which is always open night and day, here a small area called the carbon works which is a very dirty place where they produce pure carbon for batteries. Last, but not least, on this side of the hill we have the sports and social club. Here you will find all the various staff and works' canteens, a large dance hall and cricket and football pitches. The cricket pitch I am told, is almost county standard and woe betide anyone who goes on to the centre square not in cricket boots. We have an ex-county grounds man who will be out after you like a shot. Needless to say we have teams for all sports and we generally look to you young and athletic persons to play a significant part in all these activities."

"Now, that is enough from me today," said Mr Hudson rolling up his map. "Your next visit is to the Medical Centre where we give all newcomers a once over plus a more detailed talk on safety-first in a factory. I hope you all stay awake for this talk" he said, giving Roger a pointed look, "even if you have nodded off listening to me." With this final shaft of deprecatory wit he left and Roger and his group all breathed a sigh of relief.

It had been an awful lot to take in at one go. All Roger could remember was where the canteen and the sports field were, "First things first," he said to himself.

His group of new boys were then directed across to the Medical Centre which was another battered looking hut. But at least, as Roger noted when he walked in, it had the right smell of disinfectant and carbolic soap.

The talk from the doctor was very much as Roger anticipated and only one item stuck in his mind. The earnest doctor was strongly advising them against wearing any loose items of clothing or trinkets when near rotating machinery. "You're in a factory now," he said, "not at home where everything moving is tucked away. When handling lathes, milling machines, or testing rotating machinery, they are all made of steel and will take scant notice of any clothing or flesh that gets in the way. In fact they won't even slow down."

He then produced his masterpiece — a bottle full of preserving oil that had something inside that at first Roger didn't recognise. "This is the index finger of a man working on a lathe who was wearing a signet ring," he explained impressively. "He went to make some minor adjustment without stopping the lathe and the chuck block hooked inside the ring and simply pulled his finger right off." Roger stared in horror at the bottle, fascinated by the long tendons that had pulled out with the finger. They coiled round and round and were longer than the finger itself. A few years later, Roger himself was given such a ring by his wife on their wedding day. He couldn't get it off quickly enough when he got to work, and never took it to work again.

"Also," continued the doctor impressively, "when you are in main test, you will at times be testing or standing near giant machines rotating at up to three thousand revolutions per minute or 'rpm' to use our jargon. This is fifty complete revolutions every second and is a fairly common speed for electric motors. Try and imagine it! Not only do they make a considerable noise in the open air of a test environment, but the surface get hot enough to give you a severe burn. Yet would you believe it, we see apprentices, sometimes even staff, leaning over such machines at full speed to adjust testing instruments or what have you. The noise may also be almost deafening so that you won't be able to hear a single word said to you. Please give such situations every possible care."

"Too right," thought Roger "perhaps working on a farm was a safer life after all — at least you can shout at animals and whack 'em with a stick."

CHAPTER 2

"Nutcracker suite"

Large 66 kv oil circuit-breakers (left) in a substation

Roger's first post was to the Switchgear Assembly Shop, and after the dire warnings of the medical centre, he entered the shop, resplendent in his brand new overalls and toe-tectors, and prepared for the worst. His fears however were groundless, all was peace and quiet, no rotating machinery, no noise, and he was met by a congenial foreman who took him straight to a chargehand sitting on a wooden toolbox. "Here's your new apprentice Nobby," he said "Just started today so look after him won't you!" and without any more ado he wandered back to his little office, where you couldn't see the desktop, walls, or windows for papers pinned, stuck, or precariously balanced in little piles.

Nobby stood up. He was a tall, cheerful looking man, slightly balding, and he greeted Roger with a smile. Roger felt at home straightaway. "Hello son," he said, "What's your name?" Roger told him and Nobby nodded "Right, my name's Alfred, Alfred Clarke, but everybody calls me Nobby, so you had better do the same. Is this your first day?"

"Yes", said Roger, "I spent the morning being lectured in ETO, and now this is my first assignment."

"I thought so," smiled Nobby. "They often start newcomers here, I suppose it's the place where they think you can do least damage!" and he laughed. He then fired his first question and asked Roger if he had a mug.

"A mug," repeated Roger mystified. "You know, for your tea!" Nobby sounded surprised that anyone should ask such a fundamental question.

"No," said Roger "not yet."

"OK," said Nobby "I've got an old one you can use for now, but you'll have to get one of your own. It's the most important thing in these works after your birth certificate." Nobby poked around in a large box of assorted oily tools, and produced it, a rather battered mug a shade of all colours with a crude "Harry" painted around the side. "Harry was a great lad" he explained, "but has now retired. We keep his mug as a souvenir, and we use it now and then for odd jobs. We have a tea trolley come round as well" he explained, "but most of the lads don't use it, we make our own brew in the corner, they say the works' tea is only one up from rat poison." Roger looked at the mug and felt that anything drunk out of it could only be as bad. Still, he took the mug, muttered thanks, and stood awkwardly wondering what to do next.

"Your first job," said Nobby, "will be to assemble a bunch of small circuit breakers, where all the bits are here in these trays. Here is one already assembled so you can see how it goes, the only tricky bit is to fit the release spring correctly, which goes like this," and he expertly held the specimen up, juggled with a stiff spring until it came off, waved it in the air and then with a flourish fitted it back on again. "There! that's how it's done, do you think you can manage it?"

"Sure," said Roger, relieved to be given what looked a simple first task, "shall I start now?"

"If you like" said Nobby. "Tea's not due yet, but we will give you a shout" and with that he wandered off and left Roger to it.

Roger did not appreciate it at the time, but right through his time in the works, he would find there was an unwritten assumption that if someone said he could do something, he was immediately left alone to get on with it. If the person subsequently made a mess of it, there would always be someone at hand who would come up and sort out the problem; no harsh words, but maybe just a ripe swearword at the offending job itself, and, if need be, quietly get rid of any debris. This habit seemed an unwritten law, and made for a feeling of both independence and companionship that Roger came to appreciate, it stood him in good stead for the rest of his life.

"Time for my cuppa!" a voice called, and a cheerful individual plonked down comfortably beside him on a nearby toolbox, holding a large steaming mug in his hand. He was a short, quite burly man, with a very incisive voice, and exuded an air of total self-confidence, "Mind if I join you?" he started off. "My name's Fred, by the way, and I haven't seen you before have I?" he said this taking a large gulp from his mug and went on without waiting for an answer. "There's plenty here will tell you that my name always means trouble!" and he chuckled to himself.

"Why so?" stammered Roger. "My name's Roger by the way, and this is my first day here."

"I can see that by the state of your overalls, but that won't last long," said Fred and laughed at his own pleasantry with a great booming noise, rather to Roger's disquiet. "I don't work in this cosy factory," he went on "I work for the Outside Erection Division. We are the poor sods that have to make the junk you all make here actually work!"

Roger had no idea how to take this rather unexpected comment, so he only replied cautiously, "You must be joking?"

"Oh the innocence of youth," sighed Fred. "You will find out in time. Wait until you've been up all night in some draughty new building trying to get a new switchgear control panel working for the first time." He paused, and raised his voice so that many working nearby could hear him. "There are some buggers here," he went on loudly "can't tell their *left* from their *right* can they? They seem to forget that when you specify the *plus* and *minus* terminals on the back of a new meter, the office drawing assumes you are looking at it from *the front*. It doesn't help me much to find some idiot here in the works, who, when he is wiring it up from *the back,* paints a conspicuous *"plus"* and *"minus"* sign the wrong way round. The first time I find out, probably with a customer beside me, is when I finally switch on and the bloody needle goes backwards! And another thing," he went on even more loudly, "some of the wiring you buggers do is squeezed into such a small space that I am going to search for the fitter with an OBA spanner on one finger tip, and an eyeball on the other. 'cos when I do, I want to shake him by the neck." He finished his tea, yawned, stretched his legs and moved on.

Roger watched him go with mixed feelings, and started working at his circuit breakers. He found that fitting the springs was not quite as easy as it had looked. The springs were stiffer than he expected, and if he was not careful one of the wretched things would fly off, and he would need to drop the other bits, and grovel on the floor looking for the bit that had escaped. He also lost two knuckles in the next hour.

He was suddenly relieved by a general shout of "'tea'" — this time from the local tea lady trundling up with her trolley. As Nobby had predicted, many around him produced, as if by magic, mugs of all shapes and sizes already full of steaming tea, but for Roger no such delicacy was offered, and he had to make do with one from the urn which actually was not half as bad as he anticipated. Nobby came across, joined him and pointed to Roger's mug. "If you don't like that stuff, I'll get you into one of the groups who brew their own, but you'll have to take your turn at providing the necessary tea, sugar and

milk." Roger started to realise that the tea ritual was more than a drink, it was part of the shop floor religion. He really was a new boy.

"How are you getting on with the breakers?" asked Nobby sitting down on the toolbox beside him.

"Not bad," said Roger, "'I've only got a couple more to do."

"Oh Lor'!" said Nobby. "Don't go so damn fast, you'll have the shop steward on to me like a ton of bricks. All the jobs on this floor are on piece time rates, and we can't have some bright young spark rocking the boat. These breakers are rated at half an hour each! This little lot should have taken you the rest of the afternoon." He laughed at the consternation on Roger's face, "Don't worry son, you will soon get used to our ways.

Nobby changed the subject, "I saw you chatting to Fred, our perpetual pain in the arse. What d'you think of him?"

Roger paused, he was not quite sure what to say, "He seems alright," he said finally, "but he was saying some funny things."

"Oh I can guess," laughed Nobby. "No doubt he was moaning about our switchgear control panels, they are his permanent bind, but his heart's in the right place. He has a point though," he went on, "he does get some pretty complex jobs from us where the wiring at the back of the panel is already a dog's breakfast even before he starts his extra  on-site wiring to link all the kit together. But it's not really our fault. We start with a nice set of drawings, and we lay out all the switches, fuses, meters and what have you, get the holes punched through the steel panels, then sprayed, and neatly mount the front items as per the smart officially approved panel layout drawings. We then start to wire up the components from the back in a neat and logical fashion and then what do you think happens?" he asked.

"I've no idea," said Roger, who thought it all sounded fairly clear so far.

"I'll tell you what happens," carried on Nobby with a little detectable rise in his voice. "Down come the designers and say they have some brilliant new ideas, produce scrappy drawings and expect us to modify the panel on the spot. We can't say 'get knotted' of course, because they are the boss. Sometimes, it isn't even their fault, the customer himself wants the changes, and we, at the end of the chain, are expected to do miracles at the last minute. This often means having to mount extra bits on the front, and then we end up hacking them out of the polished and sprayed steel panel by hand wherever we can find a space, often not the most logical, and all the neat wiring at the back, of course, goes to absolute buggery." He finished his tea and started again. "This doesn't happen just once of course, it can happen several times. Eventually, with a bit of luck, we get a breather and get the damn thing into Despatch before they come down from the office again." He paused reflectively, "Actually, I suppose I should really take my hat off to Fred and his gangs for ever making some things work at all!"

"Do you know where these breakers go?" He asked, reverting to Roger's handiwork.

"Not really," said Roger, "although I can see how they work."

"Well," said Nobby, "They sit on some of the poles you see all over the countryside which carry electricity on overhead wires into rural districts. You may not have noticed them, but once you see the poles and wires, you will realise they are everywhere." Roger nodded, he had seen them when visiting his uncle Herb who had a farm in Henfield, a small Sussex village tucked away behind the Downs.

The memory of Uncle Herb made him smile. His uncle had woken one morning to find a new bus stop planted about one hundred yards down the road. It was for a new bus route being set up to Brighton. Thinking of the coming winter, and his own arthritis, his uncle had promptly walked down the road, dug the bus stop up, and re-planted it on the roadside just by his front door. It remained there ever after, and very convenient it was too.

Nobby finished his tea and interrupted Roger's reverie. "These breakers you are assembling go on top of some of these poles I mentioned, and switch the circuits on and off for control and re-routing purposes. They open automatically if there is an overload or short circuit on the system. Some breakers," he went on, "are more complicated and have automatic re-closing built in, you can have a go at some of these tomorrow."

"Why do they re-close," asked
Roger, who was warming to this
strange new life.

"Well" said Nobby, "very often
in country districts you get odd
overgrown trees or bits of debris
blowing around in a gale, and
these can just blow across two of
these bare overhead conductors.
This causes a short circuit, and
'bang', out comes the breaker. The
voltage between two of these
wires is 11,000, or '11 kv' in our
jargon, and the force of the short

circuit current which probably only flows for a second, is enough to
burn the twigs or what-have-you to pieces, and so the cause of the
short circuit has gone. If it has, you might as well try and re-close the
circuit straight away rather than waste an engineer's time going
round the countryside looking for a fault that isn't there anymore."

"I never thought of that," said Roger, interested.

"Ah well," laughed Nobby, "that's one of the tricks of the trade,
you'll find plenty more. These faults are called 'fleeting faults' and
happen quite often. Sometimes at home in the evenings your lights
will go off and come back on almost straight away, that's where some
breaker near you has done just this job. You can explain this to your
landlady and look intelligent," he laughed. "These attempted re-
closing take place three times if necessary to try and clear the fault.
After that, they give up, and an engineer has to come out and find the
problem. That's when you get a power cut."

"Fred came in last week with a good story," continued Nobby
laughing. "He and his gang were sitting in a field having a snack when
someone noticed a squirrel sitting on an a live over-head line busy
gnawing a cobnut, It was a very damp and windy morning, and they all
watched mesmerized as they saw the squirrel's tail getting closer and
closer to the adjoining wire. The lines were live with the usual voltage
between them of 11,000 volts. You can guess the rest," laughed Nobby.

"The poor old squirrel waved his tale once too often, and with a flash and a bang he shot ten feet into the air and came down a smoking heap!"

Roger really enjoyed the story. He had once caught a grey squirrel and it had given him a bad bite which scarred his index finger for years. He felt no sympathy at all, and for the rest of the afternoon he relished the image of the squirrel flying through the air. "Cooked supper," he thought, "for some lucky fox."

A few uneventful weeks passed and Roger, now with his own tea mug, was getting well integrated into the shop routines. He had to take his stint at greasing large 66 kv switches already mounted inside their large steel tanks, and found it was a foul, semi-dark, very cramped up job, and, as Fred had predicted, his overalls very soon started to look as mucky and battered as those around him.

"Why don't you grease up these big switches *before* you put them in the tank?" asked Roger, "it's right awkward working inside those great iron coffins."

"I know" said a non-helpful fitter, "but that's the way we do it." He laughed at Roper's look of surprise, and added apologetically. "We have tried the other way, but found that final assembly inside the tank is even more messy if everything is already covered in grease. Anyway," he added with a grin, "it gives you youngsters something to do, and gets you out of our hair for a spell."

"Thanks very much" thought Roger and pressed on.

Fred came into the shop quite often, and Roger enjoyed the pithiness of some his complaints. "His language is pretty foul at times," thought Roger, "but by jingo, his wide vocabulary and choice of expression would do credit to a high court judge." Roger found in time that many of the senior engineers he worked with had the same verbal virtuosity; it seemed an essential ingredient in getting difficult jobs done.

A new surprise greeted Roger one day. The foreman called him in and opened a conversation by saying "I hear you are the lad who keeps asking questions?"

"I suppose I do" said Roger.

"Good for you," said the foreman, "but now I've got a little job for you that I hope will test your grey matter," and he pulled out a large drawing covered in alterations in pencil. "This, believe it or not, is supposed to be the final wiring drawing for those three cabinets over there," and he pointed to a corner where three cabinets sat looking decidedly un-finished and unwanted. "The wiring team has simply given up. They complain that the outgoing terminals marked on one panel come to fifty-eight, and the next panel they link to, have only fifty-two! Plus, with all the alterations scribbled in pencil they just don't know where they are at all. See what I mean?" he added. "Unless someone sorts this out pretty damn quick, this job will fall even further behind, and I am getting it in the neck already!" He paused for breath. "What it needs is for someone to go up to the DO, that's the Drawing office, and sort them out. Don't let them fob you off, but stay with them and be a right pain in the arse until they sort it out. Do you think you can do this?"

"I suppose so," said Roger dubiously, I'll certainly have a go."

"Good on you son," smiled the foreman. "I've phoned them

up to warn them there is someone coming to sort them out, so the best of luck!" Roger picked up the drawing and left the office not at all sure he could help, or even where the DO was!

Roger, however, soon found the DO. It stretched a long way on the first floor above, and Roger soon found the right man and sorted out the problem. It was too simple for words. The wiremen were using an out-of-date drawing. Roger was able to return triumphantly to the foreman with an up-to-date drawing that made sense, and with a feeling of accomplishment. He parted from the draughtsman on the best of terms. The foreman however was not amused, he went purple. "The number of times this happens," he shouted, "one day I'll go up there and murder the bastards." Roger felt his job however was complete, and he made a diplomatic retreat.

When he got back to his job, the fitter he was working with was busy with a drill. "Ah Roger!" he said. "You've come back just right. Would you mind popping to the stores and getting me half a dozen three-eighths' holes?"

Now Roger was quite used to silly commands from his work at home on the nursery, so he answered "OK, how deep?"

"Oh about three inches will do fine," said the fitter.

"Round or square?" persisted Roger and the fitter realised that his joke was being turned against him and he laughed.

"OK, OK, you win, but we do catch 'em sometimes!"

"What happens then?" asked Roger grinning.

"I caught one out only last week," said the fitter laughing, "he actually went and asked Tom in the stores for six three-eighths' holes, and came back looking pretty sheepish. Tom had told him to come back and tell me that he only had one hole, and that was his own arse-'ole, and he was going to keep it." The fitter laughed at the memory and Roger was killing himself laughing as well.

"I can't imagine anyone actually going to ask that," laughed Roger.

"You'd be surprised," said the fitter, "We've sent lads off before now for such things as 'round ovals, six inches of three-quarter thread, striped pain't and other sillies and sometimes it works." He started to laugh again. "One of the best was old Alf telling a poor lad that he, Alf, suffered from diabetes, and could only drink pigeon's milk. The lad actually believed him and set off for the canteen right across the other side of the estate to fetch some."

"And what happened?"

"It didn't work, on the way he stopped and told his mate who of course laughed him to scorn, so he just turned round and came back looking very cross, he wouldn't speak to anyone for half-an-hour. It is part of our ritual." He continued. "We get a lot of raw beginners in here, and it's part of the fun. The options are legion. I caught one out last week when he was slow doing some filing, and I sent him off for a tin of elbow grease, and there was a lovely one last year." He suddenly recalled this and started to laugh at the memory, "Jim next door to me had a very earnest be-spectacled new graduate who will never become an engineer in a month of Sundays. Jim sent him off to the stores for a long weight." Roger stated to laugh immediately, he could see it coming. "The poor lad went off to the stores and asked for a long weight, and the store man just said 'OK' and went away. The lad stood there waiting patiently whilst two or three men came up and were served. At last, the lad asked why he wasn't being served, and when the storeman said, 'I thought you asked for a long wait' the penny at last dropped!"

"We were always doing daft requests like that at home," grinned Roger. "I remember my Dad telling a lad to go and look for a two foot length of string, pointed at both ends, with a hole in the middle, but he wouldn't go."

Fred had been listening to the conversation and joined in the laughter. "It's the same out on Erection," he grinned. "One of our common gags, when we've got to visit our substation in the Malvern Hills, where the hilltops are covered in fern, is to send a lad ahead to the council office to get a 'fern ticket'. It quite often works."

The fitter grinned, "What do you say when he comes back?"

Fred shrugged, "It depends how stupid he is. If he is a right pillock, we might send him off to the stores, perhaps to get one of my inventions, a 'splanell valve for a flunge grommet,'— that always properly fools them. We can keep some running around half the morning!"

Roger laughed. "You rotten beggars", but Fred simply grinned. "It all helps to pass the time."

Roger had passed through the DO several times before, and had been impressed by the apparent quiet and relaxed atmosphere. He had assumed it meant efficiency, but as he was to find out, it was another community that had its own ways of doing things. The head of the DO was a Mr. Ernie Balls, who was elderly, and sat in a small raised office where he commanded a good view of the forty-odd desks stretching in neat rows down the office. This position of advantage cut both ways, and there had been great merriment the day before when, whilst he was out of his office, someone had slipped a note on his desk saying, "Please ring 552 as soon as possible. Urgent." The whole office watched as Ernie came back, read the note, and proceeded to ring the number up time and time again but always found it engaged. It took over half an hour before he realised it was his own number. He glared around the office, but he had never seen so many heads down, getting on assiduously with their work.

Roger also heard how there had been a real upset some weeks earlier in the DO over the toilet routines that had grown up over many years. A lot of the draughtsmen were well set in their ways and needed a quiet time in the toilet at about nine-thirty every morning, coinciding with tea trolley time! Many brought their breakfast to work as well, and disappeared with their sandwiches into one of the row of fifteen cubicles situated in a neat row in the nearby DO lavatory. Indeed, many older draughtsmen had, by regular usage, established their own particular cubicle, and, like a favourite corner in a pub, woe betide anyone who upset the natural order of the day. "Well," explained an apprentice chuckling away, "all the doors on these cubicles had been built in the works some years earlier, and consisted of heavy steel doors on a simple 'lift up and take off the hinge design,, but as they were locally made, every door had been personally fitted and no two doors or their hinges were in exactly the same place. You can guess the rest," he chortled. "One day when me and my lads were on night shift in Big Shop, three of us came over here, took all the doors of their hinges and stacked them all mixed up in a corner. We put a note on them 'take your pick.' We were told that the next day was chaos, with draughtsmen staggering around with the heavy doors trying to find a fit. It took them nearly all the morning to sort things out, much to many draughtsmen's acute discomfort. We believe many doors ended up in the wrong place and still are. Afterwards, they said one poor soul couldn't sit down for a week!"

Fred came and sat down with Roger one day for a "cuppa", and Roger told him how he had laughed at the story of the squirrel.

"I know," smiled Fred. "It was a wet day, and the wires were a bit loose, and we all took bets with each other on how long it would be before the squirrel got blown up. I can't remember who won, but it wasn't me," and he supped his tea mournfully. "I'll tell you something I bet you don't know," he suddenly said. "Everyone thinks, when they see these poles in the ground with the wires overhead, that the poles are holding up the wires."

"How do you mean?" asked Roger "Of course they are!

"Not always," said Fred, "sometimes the wires are holding up the pole."

"How come?" said Roger expecting a funny joke.

"No, I'm serious, if you have a pole at the bottom of a dip, the wires are actually supporting the pole. Sometimes, in freezing winter days, the overhead wires shrink and tighten, and a pole at the bottom of a slope has been found pulled half out of the ground."

Roger thought for a moment, "Come to think of it, you are right." He was remembering his days in Sussex, "My uncle, who is a farmer, once knocked a pole with the combined harvester, the pole snapped clean across at the base and just stayed there swinging on the wires."

"What did he do?" asked Fred.

"Oh nothing I imagine," said Roger shrugging, "he would have left it for the electricity boys to find out themselves. I suppose it got mended one day."

"That's typical," said Fred, "we get all the other people's mistakes to put right, and all the crap when things go wrong."

Fred didn't seem particularly put out.

One day, Roger received an order from the foreman to go and get a certain design engineer and bring him down for a query on some complicated control panels. Now Roger had heard all about the eccentric group in this Switchgear Design Office and tripped up the stairs in expectation. The office was run by an engineer Mr S. A. G. Emms, and known throughout the industry for his skill and ability to "move mountains". He was known affectionately by everyone by the nickname "Skipper" as he was ex-merchant navy and held a Master Mariner's ticket. He had a trenchant turn of wit, and held a permanent view, often repeated, that all senior management were either incompetent, blind, pig-headed, or all three. He had never been sacked, as, time after time, after any argument, his comments had been proved rather too close to the mark, and his judgment, job knowledge and the devotion of everyone who worked with him always made his position impregnable. Over the next few years, Roger would become involved with him on many jobs, always getting encouragement, and never a dull moment.

Skipper was out that day, but the first thing Roger noticed was a large chair by the side of Skipper's desk, it was a large old-fashioned wooden grandfather chair with arms, and had a beautifully carved wooden seat. However, there was a large split along the grain running right through the middle of the seat, and as the chair was quite old and wobbly, anyone sitting down incautiously could get quite a nasty nip. The chair had been in that condition for as long as anyone could remember, but Skipper would not have the chair repaired as he said the chair was part of the nutcracker suite, and he didn't want to spoil the joke.

The engineers also told him that, when in the right mood, Skipper had a unique trade mark way of starting his car. It was an old open-topped Riley, with a range of bewildering knobs and pull-out adjusters on the dashboard which were of vital importance for tuning the engine when starting and running. Skipper's party-piece was to approach the car, study the weather, consider how long the car had been since last started,

and the temperature, then lean over the side, make the necessary tuning adjustment and put the vehicle into first gear. He would then walk round to the front and take a firm grip on the starting handle ready to crank the engine. Two or three deft turns were usually enough and the engine would roar into life and start to trundle forward. Skipper, who was well practiced, would smartly stand back and as the machine rumbled past, calmly step up on to the running board, lean over, grab the steering wheel, ease himself over the side, sit down on the driver's seat and be on his way.

Roger felt he wanted to learn more about this Skipper, but duty called and so he dutifully went back to the shop floor with an engineer to sort out the foreman's paperwork queries, a never- ending job. Roger excused himself and went back to his job, where he was now actually working on similar control panels. He liked the logic of control circuitry, and prided himself that he was now actually helping his mates on a better level than simply as a greaser. Before he left the foreman's office the engineer had remarked over his shoulder, "If you want to hear some real tales of our problems, come and join me at lunch."

"Fine" said Roger and went back to his job with a warm glow that he was really being accepted.

Roger went back at lunchtime and found that lunch in the Design Office was a rather ramshackle affair with engineers eating their sandwiches, still taking phone calls, and generally still arguing over problems and ideas all at the same time. It wasn't really a break from work at all. Roger had been

warned and took with him a large sausage butty from the tea trolley, the good lady always had a few with her.

"Now then, I can tell you a story that will make your hair stand on end." said the engineer spreading out his lunch, "and it is absolutely true."

"Go on" said Roger, and the engineer launched himself into his story in between munching his sandwiches.

"Over a year ago, our general site manager, Mr Gracie, called the Switchgear Manager over and announced he had some good news for him. 'Oh yes?' our Mr. Jimmy Cliff had answered cautiously, 'Yes' said Mr Gracie proudly, 'I've got you a nice big order for a new colliery winder sinking shaft with the prospects of many more to come.' Jimmy had shuddered, he already had an overstretched order book for the next two years, and this sounded ominous. Mr Gracie continued on happily, 'There's one slight complication', he said gently, 'they want delivery within twelve months' — and paused. 'Well I know you are pretty loaded at the moment, but this is a fine opportunity we cannot turn down. With the rapid growth in industry that is going on, and with hundreds of collieries either starting or changing their old steam driven winding engines into electric, the cost savings they can make are enormous, and of course the profits for our company over the next ten years can be very useful.'

"Jimmy Cliff just had to interrupt, 'Mr Gracie,' he had expostulated, 'It will be quite impossible, not only am I already stretched to full capacity, including nights, but these colliery control boards are all individual, the very devil for complexity, they give me more heartaches than all my other products put together!' 'I know I know' said our managing director 'but the company main board is involved and this has become very political, I have had no option but to agree!' 'What about our other half, the heavy engineering unit down south? Can they deliver the winding drum, all the ropes and the head gear themselves in that time?' had pursued Jimmy, 'and what about the motor itself?, have the large machine works agreed to supply in this time?', 'Apparently they have all agreed' said our proud managing director, 'including a delivery from us of a thousand horsepower induction motor, so it is all up to you.'

"Jimmy came back over here and reported this conversation to Skipper, whose job it would be, and what was said between them we can only guess." The storyteller munched happily on his sandwich. "But it would have been pretty lively to say the least," he added, and Roger, eating his own butty, agreed. He now had first-hand knowledge of this work and could imagine the panic there would be on the shop floor. "Well," continued the engineer, "we of course had to get started, and many other jobs, all wanted urgently, had to be put back. Skipper refused point blank to advise the deferred customers, 'tell that prat in admin block' he snorted. 'that he must ring up and go and see them himself, and I hope they kick his balls off.' "Another week went by," continued the story-teller, "and we received even worse news, Mr Gracie announced that the job was so important, that he himself would chair a progress meeting every two weeks. This was an unheard of intrusion into our Switchgear Division. He really knew nothing about the work, and we shuddered at the implications. Skipper suggested that we sat him in the nutcracker chair, but he said it would be a waste of time, he wouldn't feel a thing!"

Now Roger had already been exposed to a very common practice on the shop floor caused by the frequent delays of deliveries from outside suppliers of vital parts such as display ammeters and voltmeters. Often, for example, a whole switchboard could be finished except for the fitting of a single meter, Roger had more than once been given the task of searching round other boards being assembled to see if he could spot one. If he found one, it would be up to the gang leaders to agree a possible exchange for some other favour. Roger remembered the problem vividly as the engineer continued with his story. "Well," he continued, "many other jobs on the shop floor soon came to a grinding halt as components were taken from them to get these blessed new set of panels finished on time. There were many angry scenes on the shop floor as you can imagine! Mr Gracie, however, whom God preserve, carried on chairing his progress meetings with a smile on his face, nodding with approval at the progress, but with no idea of the mayhem going below."

"Did you succeed?" asked Roge.

"Well, yes and no" replied the storyteller with a huge grin on his face. "We actually finished the panels on time, but about a month before we were ready to deliver, our Outside Erection staff paid a visit to the site where the new sinking shaft was supposed to be, and were astonished to find nothing there, only a green field. Thinking some mistake about the site whereabouts, we phoned up the customer and asked for direction. After a pause, a very apologetic, Welsh voice, answered, 'Ah boyo, haven't you been told? we haven't started yet!' he paused, 'We have had problems with the planning you see, we shan't want the winder for another twelve months, d'you see? I'm very sorry that no one has told you, but it's been rather out of our hands d'you see.'

"As you imagine, Mr. Gracie was mortified and I don't think he showed his face in Switchgear Division for another twelve months," laughed the storyteller

"What did you do?" asked Roger.

"Well, things like this have happened before, and we simply shipped the finished panels out to Birmingham airport where we keep a hangar, and placed it under lock and key. But you won't believe the final bit" he added with an even bigger grin. "Although the panels were locked away intact, word got around the shops. There are several

keys to the hangar, and over the next year many useful bits were surreptitiously lifted for other vital jobs. When the panels were eventually wanted, now of course in a hurry again, the shift leader whose job it was, opened up the hangar and found not much more than a skeleton!"

Roger joined in the laugh, and went back to his post shaking his head, a "sadder and a wiser man" he mused, thinking of the Ancient Mariner from some earlier scrap of school poetry.

CHAPTER 3

"Whoops!"

A large 300/132 kV transformer in its tank

After his stint in Switchgear, which he left with some regret, Roger's next post was to the Transformer Division. The building was adjacent to Switchgear, and some areas were shared so again he found himself getting lost. There was an important section surrounded by an iron screen, and used by both Switchgear and Transformer for high voltage testing. Right from the outset Roger found the work and atmosphere entirely different. For the first time he came across a bay entirely staffed by women of all ages, and quite different to the girls he had spent happy hours with back at home on the village green. These girls were much tougher, intent on getting on with their work, but, like everywhere else, basically friendly. But, "By Jingo," thought Roger after he had been there a few weeks, "their language, when teased or provoked, is out of this world." Within a few weeks he had learned a colourful vocabulary he had never dreamt of "and much of it from very innocent looking young ladies too," he mused, blushing inwardly. Yes — he still had a lot to learn.

The new foreman was a quick speaking and dapper individual and he started by giving Roger a quick overview of the work. "One of the key problems in this shop is cleanliness. We are not like many other shops where muck and rubble is unavoidable," he stressed. "The work here is mainly an assembly job where we start with very clean components, and build up the transformers, put them in a steel tank, fill it with oil, and then test it. The least traces of dirt or grease inside

will be fatal because of the high voltages we deal with. Once in service, these voltages inside the transformer have a nasty knack of worming their way through any suspect spots of dirt, grease, or untidy bits of material, and cause internal sparks."

He paused for effect. "This can lead to an internal fire, maybe an explosion and the transformer is of course ruined, and our name's mud."

"Can't you check before it is all put together?" asked Roger.

"Yes, of course we do!" replied the foreman. "We keep checking at every blessed stage. But it's the last high voltage tests at the end that are the worst. We can't apply the full working voltages, which go up to two hundred and seventy-five thousand on the big ones, until the beast is in its tank and filled with oil."

"Two hundred and seventy-five thousand volts?" repeated Roger in awe. "That's incredible! Do you really mean it? Inside this factory?"

"Yes, that's right," said his guide, pleased to see the astonishment on Roger's face. "And we are now doing tests up on the hill at four hundred thousand. It is going to be the next national and international standard." "Wow," said Roger, at a loss for words "I can't imagine it! Our supply voltage at home is, of course, only two hundred and forty if we're lucky, and that's enough to kill us! I can't even imagine voltages up in the hundreds of thousands, and inside this building too. Is it safe?"

His guide laughed "Don't worry! All the big voltages are inside that enclosed cage over there. If you behave yourself, you might get in there yourself to help one day, but it will be near the end of your apprenticeship."

"Wow" said Roger again, realising his vocabulary was whittling down to next to nothing!

Roger pulled himself together. "I was asking," he said, "why do you wait until the transformer is full of oil before you apply the high voltage tests? It must be an awfully messy job to drain the oil off and do repairs if you find a fault? I've been told in the ETO what deadly stuff transformer oil is."

"You're damn right," said his guide, "but this wretched transformer oil is an essential part of the high voltage insulation. Without the oil, the high voltages would flash all over the place and the unit would blow up. We don't muck about with high voltages," he added, "the forces are enormous." The foreman was obviously enjoying his little lecture. "So, for example," he grinned, "talking about dirt, don't go anywhere near the coil winding shop in dirty overalls, it's full of ladies, and if you go in dirty, you'll get an earful you won't forget." This was a useful warning that would serve Roger well.

He began life in this new shop by being taken round for a walk. He was grateful for this, for in Switchgear it had taken several weeks before he had understood only half the whole picture. "We take you round here," said a rather harassed looking charge hand, "because in this shop we can tell a decent story that visitors just about understand. No other shop can do this because it's either too dangerous, too noisy, or too much of a bloody shambles to let visitors in. You'll get this guide job yourself soon," he suddenly added, "we old hands get fed up of doing it. Sometimes management think we've nothing better to do."

"Well," he went on, "we start here with the winding shop, where you can see these ladies turning rolls of bare copper strip into neat coils, with the copper tightly bound with insulating tape" The girls were seated in front of complicated Heath Robinson type machines that first wound insulating tape on to the wire, which slowly unrolled from a drum. Then the girls guided the moving strip on to a former which wound it into a hollow coil, at the same time counting the number of turns. "The skill with this job" said his guide, "is in keeping the coils accurate, clean, and with the right number of turns. They have to be exactly the correct size as stated on the drawing or else they won't fit when we come to assemble them. In this bay, nearly every job is different to the last one, and the girls have to be on their toes all the time."

"That's right ducks", said one of the girls near them, "but we don't stay on our toes all night!" and a great guffaw came from the group around her.

"Keep your dirty mind to yourself Masie," said the guide. "This young man here might be your managing director one day!"

"Oh, we could *manage* him all night," came Masie's immediate reply, eyeing Roger up and down with a saucy grin. All the girls around started laughing and staring at Roger, who stood there feeling completely tongue-tied.

"Come on", said his guide laughing, "we'd better get out of here before they get rude."

"Are they always like this?" asked Roger.

"Only when they see someone in trousers, but this is nothing," said his guide, "you wait until Christmas Eve," a cryptic remark that, at the time, went over Roger's head. They continued their tour, stopping in the assembly area where they built up transformer cores from thin sheets of iron laid one on top of each other in a careful pattern. Then it was on to where they fitted the coils over the cores, and then to where they were tanked up and filled with oil. "Now," said his guide with a final flourish, "here is the dreaded test area, where occasionally several months' work might fail, and much of it have to be done over again. But we don't say that bit to visitors," he said with a grin.

It was time for a cup of tea, and Roger and his guide sat down on some toolboxes. "You bloody apprentices," said his guide suddenly, "they'll drive me nuts one day." He showed Roger his mug, a brand new enamel one, white with a blue rim. "Look at this," he said "I've just had to buy this. What do think happened to my old one?"

"I've no idea," said Roger, wondering what was coming.

"It was a decent mug," continued his guide, "still in good nick, and good for another ten years. Then this very funny apprentice comes along with a nail, bangs it through the bottom and nails it to the bench. He then filled it with boiling hot tea and told me my tea was ready." "You can laugh!" said his guide as Roger couldn't contain himself, "but I was the laughing stock of the place! If I could have caught 'im, I would have murdered him, but by then the little bugger had run off! It took me a few minutes to work out what had happened and some time to clear up the mess."

He brooded for a while on the memory, "You can't do much with a scalding cup of tea nailed to your desk!" he suddenly added, looking gloomily into his new mug and sipping slowly.

Roger did his best not to laugh, and changed the subject. "They told us in ETO to try and avoid answering any questions from visitors on how transformers work, have you ever been asked?"

His guide put down his mug. "I'm always being asked this," he replied, "and I took the trouble once to work out an answer. Unless we say something to shut them up, there's always some Charlie who keeps coming back to it and holding up the walk around. What I do is explain it like this," and he drew a long breath and started. "When we place a coil over an iron loop, that is the core, and then when we place a voltage on the coil, a current flows in the coil, and the iron core becomes magnetised. We call this a magnetic flux in the iron core, which you can't see, but it turns the core into a sort of very large magnet and it spreads a flux field all around. However, because this is an alternating current, going plus and minus fifty times a second, this flux is also pulsating just the same. You can hear the core buzzing, and if the core is not well made, this noise can be very loud because any loose piece of iron lamination will buzz like a siren. Now, if you put another coil over the first one, the pulsating flux excites this second coil and generates a voltage in it. If you have different numbers of turns on the two windings, you get different voltages on them. This is called the transformer action, and means we can change the voltages on the network up and down as required. This transformer action only works with alternating current, and that is why *AC* became universally adopted around the turn of the century. Until then, there had been a lot of *DC* or direct current supplies like the output from a battery, but you were stuck with the *DC* voltage of the battery."

"I know," said Roger. "With *AC* when the voltage goes up, the current comes down to supply the same power. If you didn't have transformers, you couldn't deliver electricity from a modern power station at all! The currents coming out would be enormous. I worked out once that instead of transmission by thin wires, you would need to have a load of copper conductors coming away from the power station of well over three feet square each."

"That's a nice one," approved his guide, "I might use that myself in the future."

Roger's first job was in a core assembly area, and he found the work quite tricky. He was apprentice here to a staff man, and the task was to build up this iron core from thin sheets of metal, pre-cut from guillotines in another area, and needing a wide range of shapes for any one core. The task was to lay the correct pieces down one by one, forming an E-shape lying on the floor with a crossarm or yoke across the top. All the pieces had exact dimensions for the build, each corner having to have a very exact butt joint. The yokes top and bottom were wider than the three limbs, and to further complicate matters, the width of the strips up each limb varied, starting small, and getting wider at the centre, and then down again to the top. This ensured

"Dad, you promised me five shillings for every exam I passed and I passed two!"

"Here's ten shillings, but don't study so hard."

a reasonably round section through the stack when placed upright, and thus allowed a neat fit for the coils which slipped over the three limbs without a big waste of space. There were bolt holes also already punched though the sheets and so positioned that if the core was correctly assembled, fixing bolts could be pushed through to allow the sheets to be clamped tightly together. Any slight untidiness in only one sheet would mean that when finally clamped up, the bolts would not slide through. When this happened, Roger was to discover, the language became an education in itself. A large transformer would have several thousand sheets of these iron laminations, and weigh many tons.

Roger studied the jigsaw puzzle of the job, and silently marvelled at the designer who'd come up with it. Suddenly he had an inspired thought. "We can't do it like this?" he said, "we haven't got the coils here! It's no use putting this top yoke on until the coils are on!"

"Aha young man! that's where you're wrong," said the fitter. "What we have to do, is complete the core including the top yoke, have it tested and if OK send it on to assembly. There, they take all the top sheets of iron out again, place the coils on, and put the top yoke back again sheet by sheet."

"What?" exclaimed Roger "half our careful work is undone, and then someone puts it all back again?"

"Afraid so," laughed the fitter. "Over the years many have tried to find a better way, but no one has ever come up with one. If you can think of one, I tell you now, you'll make your fortune."

"I'll think about it," thought Roger to himself. But over the next month, he realised maybe conventional wisdom and practice had got it right.

Towards the end of the afternoon, Roger noticed a number of workers with their coats on coming through the shop and gathering furtively near the large door at the end. Some were pushing bicycles. "What's going on there?" he asked.

"You might well ask," said his mate. "It's getting near quitting time, and that door is the nearest to the main gate. Every day we get people drifting through here from all corners of the factory, ready to make a dash for it when the hooter goes. It's a bloody nuisance, and the works' police are supposed to have stopped it, but as soon as they turn their backs, it starts to build up once again. They are supposed to stop pilfering as well, but it's a never-ending job. There's many a house in this district with a few bits of company property in useful places!"

Sure enough, when the hooter went, there was a mad scramble of bodies charging out the door and flying off down the avenue, some almost running, and others leaping on bikes which had appeared from nowhere. Roger felt a bit depressed by the sight, picturing the opening of the Bastille during the French Revolution. Back on the farm in Sussex, he recollected, one gauged one's work by the size of the job, not by the clock. Here, he had seen a plumber sawing through a pipe with a hacksaw, and as soon as the hooter sounded, he left his saw halfway through the pipe, put on his coat and went home. Roger went to the door and watched. He noticed the works policemen standing by helplessly looking sharply at everyone, and giving an impression of being alert to any suspicious bulges in coats.

A 33 kV winding coil for a large transformer

The works, police, he found in time, were a continual source of jokes and stories by apprentices. One he heard back at the Hall concerned a tale of a man who came to the main gate one wet day pushing a wheelbarrow. The storyteller explained, "The wheelbarrow was stacked high with straw, covered by a sheet of cardboard and tied down with string to keep the drizzle out. The policeman on duty came out of his hut in his duffle coat, and wanted to know what was going on. The man replied that he had collected a load of waste packing straw from Incoming Stores and was taking it home for his daughter for her pet rabbits. The policeman gingerly lifted the corner of the cardboard and gave a cursory poke round under the straw, found nothing, and let him through. Being the day it was, the copper didn't want to hang about outside, and the more he poked about, the more bits of wet straw blew out and started to stick all along the main drive. And that," said his storyteller, "would worry the copper more than the wheelbarrow load." The storyteller chuckled, "This pantomime happened again a few weeks later, and it wasn't until the third time that someone on duty realised the man was actually stealing wheelbarrows." Roger never knew whether or not this story was true, there were times when he found truth was stranger than fiction in this place, so he let it go.

While still in Transformer Works, Roger had his first encounter with a woman who was universally feared. She was the secretary to the works director, a certain Miss Howard, and had an office next to the managing director's. She had her own assistant, and appeared to have a great deal of authority. She was known by everyone as "Dolly" and was the only female in any of the management teams. She was as masculine in her approach as any of the men around her and her language, when roused, could match anyone's. She was rumoured to have had a significant hand in all major promotions or discipline problems on the site, and could ridicule any person she thought was not up to the mark with a withering comment "Hugh,— him! He doesn't know whether his arsehole's punched or bored". This became her trademark expression. One day, still in his early days as an apprentice, Roger was summoned to her presence concerning an article he had written for the apprentice's newsletter known affectionately as the "Apes Journal". He had already been introduced to this internal quarterly magazine which was light hearted and edited entirely by apprentices. Roger had met the editor early in his stay and had been pressed into making a contribution; the editor was always looking desperately for more copy. However, before the publication of the regular six hundred copies, the draft had to be submitted to the manager of ETO for approval. Being slightly fearful of some of the apprentices' sense of humour, he always sought a second opinion. Dolly had seized on this job as her own, after all, it could be a useful source of information!

As Roger was a new contributor, he had been summoned to see her. She always made a point of seeing new contributors, supposedly to encourage them. But it always turned out to be a veiled warning. As she said to all of them, "Your apprentices' magazine goes out to our branches all around the world, and we have no control over in whose hands it finishes up. It sets the tone of our company. We don't want any smutty jokes or cartoons, or any articles that are seriously critical of any person or department, do you understand?"

"You bet we did," explained the editor to Roger, and now they both found themselves called to her palatial office.

Roger's very first words to Dolly were a mistake. No one had warned him she only had one arm that finished at the elbow joint. Roger had heard so much about Dolly that he had imagined a sort of all powerful Amazon of a lady, absolutely perfect in every respect. When he and the editor walked into Dolly's office she told them curtly to sit down, and stood up to reach over for the journal script on a pile of papers. It was then that Roger saw she only had the one complete arm, and some instinctive reaction in Roger that he never understood made him blurt out, "You've only got one arm!" The silence in the room was deafening. Dolly just glared at him, and in utter confusion Roger stammered, "I'm sorry, but nobody told me." For some reason, this seemed to satisfy Dolly, nothing more was said, and they got on discussing the draft script as though nothing had happened. She had a few comments about the magazine not being as good as it used to be and after a few standard introductory remarks to Roger, the pair were dismissed.

"My God," said the editor wiping his brow as they left, "that will be all round the works tomorrow. That's the first time I've seen Dolly not know what to say."

Roger went back to his work, and found the fitter he was working with struggling with a new drawing. He was trying to fold it and get it supported on his desk so it would be easy to read as they worked. It was for the next core they had to assemble, and he was getting frustrated. "Ah Roger!" he said sounding exasperated. "This bleedin' drawing is a bugger, would you pop down to the coil winders and ask Masie for a stand. A two-foot stand will be about okay. She'll know what you want."

"Sure!" said Roger and off he went and found the winder girls busily at work. "Masie!" he said happily, "Jack has sent me over to get a two-foot stand. He says you will know what I want." Masie looked at him with a straight face, and all the girls near her stopped work.

"A two-foot stand?" queried Masie, "I'm not sure about two *feet*," she said very contemplatively, looking Roger up and down, and turned round to her neighbours "Girl's what do you think? Can any of you help this young man?" Great grins were spreading across their faces as they all eyed poor Roger up and down. "I could probably give you a six-inch stand – just about," said Molly sounding helpful, and they all burst into roars of raucous laughter. Roger turned crimson with embarrassment. It suddenly dawned on him they were all referring to a male erection!

"Oh boy," he said to himself. "The devils, they've really caught me this time," and he hurried back to Jack with the sound of hoarse throaty cackles ringing in his ears. Back at the desk, he found Jack had the drawing already neatly in position.

"Any luck?" he asked with a straight face, and Roger could only grin at him.

"You beggar! you got me properly this time," he admitted, and Roger now saw that half the fitters in the bay had been in on the joke and were all standing around looking delighted.

Most of the transformers being built were too heavy to lift by hand, and overhead cranes were in use all the time. For the large units, standing ten feet tall, the very heavy master cranes were needed. Slinging these was an art in itself, and the task of manipulating heavy steel wire ropes into the right positions was critical, and then seeing the crane gently take the strain was the work of experienced men. This lifting of large transformers and moving them down the shop, over the heads of many working staff was a standard practice, and the workers underneath and took no notice. Roger, however, stood watching fascinated and fearful as one of these giant weights, swaying gently on their hawsers, was slowly working its way from one station to another. "We dropped one of those big buggers a couple of years ago," a voice said suddenly, and Roger turned to see an old hand standing next to him. "You've never seen such a cock-up in your life," he continued.

"Was anyone killed?" asked Roger turning to him in amazement.

"No thank goodness," said the man. "We were lucky. We were just lifting it from its spot to put it in its tank, it needed two cranes, one each end, and as it rose to about ten feet in the air, one of the cranes slowed down whilst the other carried on lifting. Before anyone could stop it, the unit tipped sideways, toppled over with the weight, and came crashing down. The men around it saw it starting to topple, and just ran hell for leather out the way. The noise was tremendous, you could hear it all over the factory, and a great cloud of dust rose so that you couldn't see a thing. When the dust settled we could see that the clamps had broken, and there was a great pile of twisted windings, loose steel laminations, and general chaos all over the floor!" The old hand shook his head again at the memory. "What a mess it was, and what a commotion! The news spread round the factory, and before anyone could restore order, hundreds of workers from everywhere were pouring in to see what had happened. The rumour got around that it was an unexploded wartime bomb, the noise would have been about the same."

Roger's mind was in turmoil trying to imagine the scene "What on earth did you do?" he asked.

The old hand smiled and shrugged his shoulders. "Well, we just had to sort it all out. It took us about two weeks to clear up the mess, and get work going normally, and two months to rebuild the transformer." Roger supposed it was all in the day's work in this factory, but he watched the cranes far more closely for the rest of his stay.

CHAPTER 4

"What did you say?"

Examining a motor stator before adding the rotor

Roger only spent one month in Transformer Work. He was told that with so much to learn in his two years, a month in Transformers was all there was time for. "Just as well!" he thought, he had not got used to the heavy loads swinging overhead, and there had been quite a lot of standing about with not much to do.

His next post was to Standard Test, where he was warned that life would be a very different kettle of fish compared to his posts so far. As soon as he walked in, Roger understood what they meant. He was hit by the very big difference. "Boy, is this place noisy!" he said to himself.

There was a continual barrage of noise as soon as he went through the door. There were motors and generators running on test wherever there was a space, with men and apprentices standing over them, either taking readings, checking temperatures, or busy setting up further machines for test. Everyone seemed to accept the noise, aggravated by testers standing close to each other and shouting into each other's ears. "How the devil do they hear each other in this racket?" thought Roger, "I shall need some earplugs." However, after a few introductions, he was soon to learn that nobody used earplugs, it was out of the question. When he asked why not, the foreman just laughed.

"Earplugs would be no good in this place," he explained. "You need to be alert all the time to the slightest change in the noise of the machine you are testing. You'll soon get used to it!" He then added as an afterthought, "In any case, with earplugs in, you might miss the tea trolley, and that wouldn't do would it?" and with that apparent shaft of wit the subject was dropped

.

The main task here was to wire up a new motor or generator to a supply, and then give it a thorough testing before despatch. The accepted requirement was a "heat run", which entailed coupling the new machine to a parent works' machine so that the new machine could be loaded up to full load. A range of thermometers and meters were stuck on the new machine, currents and voltages had to be recorded, and a graph had to be plotted of the rise in temperature at a number of positions on the machine as it ground away on full load. The test run could need several hours until all the thermometers were registering a final steady state temperature. The motors and generators being tested covered a wide range of important industrial activities such as tram motor and train drives, mining ventilation pumps, oil refinery pumps, ship supply generators and indeed, every job seemed different. It was explained to Roger that these tests were necessary as once these machines were on customer premises, they might end up in various inaccessible positions where they were expected to run without trouble for maybe twelve months or more without any attention. The range, sizes and types of motor were wide, and suddenly

Roger found himself having to think carefully back to his technical training at college to appreciate just how some of the tests could be wired up and conducted

Roger's first task was to go and collect a set of cables to wire up the next job. "Right-ho" he said cheerfully, "where do you keep cables?" He thought this was a sensible question, but it was met with a loud guffaw and he was pointed to the far corner. There he found a great pile of discarded odds and ends of cables, all thicknesses and lengths with no indication of their suitability for any required voltages or currents. "Use your loaf," was the only advice he was given. On top of that, many had seen better days, and one had to untangle a piece, not an easy job for the heavier pieces, and examine it for cuts and missing insulation. Also, Roger found that the ends were often so chewed up with having been repeatedly screwed up with a nut and bolt that a new clean end had to be scraped clean and prepared.

Then Roger found another snag. Although there were neat terminals on the new machine, he was expected to look anywhere for some convenient nuts, bolts, and washers to connect on the test cables. "Is there any guidance on this?" he asked.

"Is there heck" he was told. "Look around and grab anything handy to secure your cables properly," and with this minimum amount of information he started to work. If all this wasn't bad enough, finding the requisite test voltmeters and ammeters soon proved to be another trial. "We are always short of the bloody things," he was told, "have a good look round, and see what you can scrounge."

"What a way to run an army!" thought Roger, but kept his thoughts to himself. Once Roger started on

"I refuse to switch off until you stop swearing."

the work however, he found that, somehow or other, things seemed to sort themselves out, there was plenty of help when he asked, and it wasn't too long before he had his first motor, a new Express Lift main drive motor, all wired up and ready for inspection. A senior tester came over, checked it all carefully, and then grunted, "That's fine, we'll give it a spin soon, but first, it's time for the tea break," and he led Roger to a comfortable corner where most of the testers were already seated on their toolboxes with the proverbial mugs in front of them, and with some also busy munching into their breakfast butties.

Roger noted with a wry smile that all the tests were still going on, but left with apprentices to keep an eye on them. "This place wouldn't work without the apprentices," he mused, and sat down gratefully for a mug of tea that he felt he had really earned.

One of the senior testers, a tough looking man in his thirties turned to Roger and started a friendly conversation by asking Roger how long he had been an apprentice and where he came from. "Oh, I'm still a bit of a new boy," answered Roger. "I grew up in Sussex, and I came up here to the Midlands for the first time this August."

"Sussex!" exclaimed his questioner. "Sussex! that's the worst place on this earth, I had the worst time of my life down there. What a dump it is." Roger looked startled, but before he could say a word the tester carried on. "I was down there in the army in 1943, and we were out doing army training on the Sussex Downs, digging trenches in January into that frozen chalk, with rain and a bitter wind tearing us to pieces. It was an awful time, and I can still feel it in my bloody bones to this day!" Those around him laughed, and Roger joined in.

"Whereabouts on the Downs were you?" asked Roger
. "It was a god-forsaken place called Cissbury Ring," came the unexpected reply, "just north of Worthing."

"Blow me," said Roger in astonishment "that's where I come from, Cissbury Ring was our playground! Me and our gang spent hours up there in the summertime. It was only about fifteen minutes jog from our village green, and we would often spend all day up there just messing round. We really loved it up there!"

"Well I'm buggered," laughed the Tester, "but you couldn't get up there during the war, the Army had taken it over."

"That's what you think!" said Roger, "we used to go up there just the same. We used to run up there after school and the weekends, and go up to our usual playground spots. They were our Downs you see!"

"But weren't you ever stopped?" asked the tester.

"No chance," said Roger. "Often there was no one about, but sometimes soldiers or police did try to catch us, but they had no chance. We were all as fit as fleas, could run like hares, and we knew every inch of the area like the backs of our hands."

"But it was very dangerous", the tester pursued, "After night exercises, there were often bits of dangerous live ammunition left hanging about."

"Quite right, there were," agreed Roger, "we used to collect lots."

"Collected!" exclaimed the ex-soldier in amazement. "Collected what, for God's sake?"

"Well, souvenirs of course, we collected all sorts of bullets, bombs and flares and other interesting things, and there was a roaring trade between us in swaps when we got home. I know our parents were very often worried about it all, and there were a number of nasty accidents, but not in our gang," he said, reminiscing. "But some did. For example, one stupid lad took home a three-inch high explosive mortar bomb, put it into his father's vice in the garden shed, and tried to saw the end off. He was killed of course, and there were several incidents of boys losing hands or getting badly burnt."

"Hell's teeth," said another listener. "Surely the police could stop it all?"

"They did their best, I suppose," said Roger, "they used to come round the schools giving lectures, and so did the army. In fact, the lectures were very useful," continued Roger, "because they brought us examples of things that were deadly so that we knew what to avoid. It didn't stop us going up there, but it helped us to be careful."

"Well, I'll go to Jericho," exclaimed a listener. "It's a wonder any of you are still alive!"

The tea break came to an end, and they all reluctantly left their toolboxes with several testers wanting to hear more from Roger about his war stories. Roger was quite surprised at their interest, as it didn't seem at all unusual to him. There had never been any sense of danger he thought, just the excitement of the treasure hunts as they had called them. He remembered one real laugh they had when a lad at school brought in a bullet head, and asked them what it was. The lad could see it was a bullet of course, but he was curious about the back end which was a hard smooth grey colour. He guessed it was the lead filling which he wanted to get out for modelling purposes. It was still early in the war, and Roger recalled the lads in his class were all still a bit green. They passed the bullet around between them, and all agreed with the owner about the lead, and advised him to hold it in the fire in some tweezers, and catch the lead as it melted.

The lad came to school next day in a rare old state. He had done what they had suggested, and held the bullet over the sitting room fire in the evening when all the family were around, and after a few minutes, there was suddenly a bang and a fizzing noise, and the bullet flew around the room filling it with smoke and muck. It was a tracer bullet! His mother nearly had a fit. No damage had been done, but the room was a real mess, although thank goodness no one was hurt. His dad had really given him a hard time over it, and he was banned from any more collecting of anything. It wasn't really his fault, he said, everyone was collecting souvenirs, and he had been careful and asked for our advice. He had found the bullet lying in the road after one of the early "Battle of Britain" dog fights that were often going on high above us.

Roger went back to the machine he had wired up, the tester was with him, and they started up the motor with no problem. The noise was quite high, but Roger found that he was already getting used to it, and had no problems listening to the tester. He found the work interesting, as the regular logging of all the readings made him realise that there was more about the motor than just going round! The tester made him feel the bearings to check for any vibration or getting hot, the current and voltage had to be checked, and the speed was monitored all the time. They had stuck thermometers on to the motor with plasticine, and these were recording the temperature of the motor and the output flow of air from a built-in fan at the end of the motor. The output thermometer was the most important, he was told. "That tells us whether everything inside the machine is 'OK'. "It's the key figure to record, and we carry on this run until that settles down at its steady state expected temperature." The tester then added, "That will take about two hours for this machine, and is the most important figure both for the Design Office and the customer."

Roger soon began to realise that this testing was the easy part, getting the machines ready was often more difficult. Apart from the usual scramble to find all the cables and meters, some machines needed more elaborate set-up arrangements, and he found the variety interesting although the routine heat runs afterwards were sometimes a bit of a bore. One irritant was the fact that the testers made all the decisions, they were often too busy to really answer Roger's questions, and he found, as he suspected the first day, that the apprentices were the basic dogsbodies of the department.

There was however, excitement one day, when a machine that had been running on test for nearly an hour, suddenly began to show an unexpected rising of temperatures. Roger called the tester over, and whilst they were both looking at the readings, smoke began to pour out the end, together with some sparks and a smell of burning. "Oh shit!" said the tester, shutting the set down immediately.

"Don't touch anything!" said the tester "this doesn't happen very often, but we now call down the Design Office to take over."

"What do you think is wrong?" asked Roger.

"I've no idea," said the Tester, "this is a new design, and it could be anything from a design that can't take the load, to a simple bit of insulation inside that has come loose. By the way, thanks for spotting it straight away. Sometimes, when we are not sharp enough, the damn thing gets really on fire and burns out." Roger felt pleased with the compliment, and just grinned. The tester explained, "If it is totally burnt out, we get a

bollocking from Design for not being awake, and they have lost any chance of finding out the cause. As for this one, I'm sure they'll open up and find the problem. All the readings we have taken will also be a big help. Well done!" Roger really felt pleased with himself, this time all the donkey work had been really necessary!

A few days later, Roger found himself once again having his tea break alongside the ex-army tester who had been up on the South Downs during the war. "Ah good," said the tester making himself comfortable on the well worn toolbox, "I've been dying to see you again to ask you more about when you went collecting your "souvenirs". I still shudder when I think of the stuff that we used to leave hanging around."

"Well, we were fairly careful of course," said Roger "there were some things we were looking for especially, and on the whole, if we had no idea what something was, we just stayed clear."

"What were you looking for then?"

"There were several things that were real prizes. Live 0.303 ammunition was highly sort after as well as those great 'thunder-flash' fireworks, because you couldn't buy fireworks during the war. The best finds of the lot were unexploded two-inch mortar bomb parachute flares, we loved finding those."

"Good God above!" exclaimed the tester, "but they look the same as the two-inch high explosive mortars."

"Not quite," said Roger happily, "the 'HE' ones had a thin red ring round them, and our gang left them alone. Some-times" added Roger, thinking back wistfully, "if they had been fired from the mortar and not gone off, the bombs were quite dirty and it was difficult to pick out those with a red ring. But in the end our gang never made any mistakes thank goodness."

"Christ Almighty!" explained one of the listeners "I can't believe I'm hearing this."

"It's quite true" protested Roger, "I had a lovely pile of souvenirs by the end of the war."

"Where are they now?"

"That's an aggravating story," went on Roger "but after I had gone to college, my mother found all this 'junk' as she called it, all lying around in a shelf in the shed and getting all corroded, so she called someone in and had it all taken away."

"Best thing she could do," was the general agreement all round.

The tester persisted. "Yes, but what did you do with this live stuff you took home. Was that left in the shed?"

"Oh no" explained Roger, that was all used up. We used to organise firework parties and really enjoy ourselves."

"How?" they all asked. "Well, the prize things were the mortar flares, because we could put them in the vice and saw the end off, and first get out the lovely pure silk parachute inside. These were a real prize, they were about six foot in diameter of real silk, and were in great demand by the ladies. You couldn't get silk any other way in the war. Then you could tip out the pure magnesium powder which was a grey powder, wonderful stuff, and use it to make fireworks."

"Go on" said the listeners. Roger continued happily, he was well away into fond memories.

"The problem with magnesium powder is how to set it alight, as you need a higher temperature than you can get with a match. But then someone came up with the solution. We took the live .303 ammunition, put them in the vice and wrenched the bullet heads off, and tipped out the cordite. The cordite was in thin yellowy strips like very thin lengths of straight macaroni, and you then stood the empty cartridge case on the wall and filled it with magnesium powder, and stuck two strips of the cordite in the top. They made absolutely marvellous fireworks. You could stick a row of them upright on the wall and then light the top of the cordite, this burnt down with a satisfactory flame and splutter, and its temperature was sufficient to ignite the magnesium. Then you got a magnificent firework display, better than any fireworks you had ever had before the war. As they burned, they spouted a great tongue of pure white light into the air. We used to light them at night, of course, and you could see for miles! At the end came a nice surprise. The heat from the burning magnesium set off the percussion caps at the bottom of the cartridge case, this caused quite a large final bang and the case flew off anywhere. They were great shows!"

There was silence for a minute, then one of the elder testers remarked, "I think I was safer up here being bombed, than down in your place with you kids mucking about like that!" and among general agreement and laughter, they all finished their tea and went back to work.

Back at the Hall that evening, Roger was telling his pals about life in Standard Test, and mentioned his view that he was being used as a bit of a dogsbody, the testers made all the decisions, and were often too busy to explain what they were doing.

"It's a standard problem in that shop," one of his pals explained "But why don't you go on night shift?"

"Why so?" asked Roger surprised, "what's the difference?"

"Plenty!" said his pal, "On night shift, if they take to you, they just let you get on with the job yourself, let you do it all on your own, right from wiring up to writing the final test report."

"And they take their time too!" interrupted another lad. "They never seem to be in a hurry on nights, everyone takes their time, and the night shift chief often retires to his office after the tea break and we don't see him again."

"The tea breaks often get stretched too," said his pal, "and you will hear plenty of stories about the works whilst you are there. It's a social education. I went on night shift there and thoroughly enjoyed it."

Roger was intrigued by this advice, and next day went to the ETO to ask if he could also make the change. "Sure," said the affable Mr Hudson "I think you could do it, your record so far is quite good. One graduate is moving on from there next week, and you can take his place. But they are a bit choosy there, if they don't think you are capable of being left alone, they very quickly give me a ring and you will be moved."

Roger swallowed hard, "Well, I've understood everything so far, so I think I shall be OK."

"Good lad," said Mr Hudson "I'll fix for you to start next Monday."

Next Monday evening, Roger had the strange experience of cycling into the works in the dark for his first spell on night shift. It was now wintertime, and it was a dark and gloomy evening. He had never been in the works before at night, and quite suddenly, all the buildings that he had never noticed before, now seemed to loom in sinister ways as he strode past them from the cycle racks. Most of the shops were empty and closed, all the roadways were deserted, and the silence gave the whole works an eerie and ghostly atmosphere so different to the hustle and bustle during the day. There were small lamplights glowing through the gloom at all the corners, and he hurried past some dark alleyways wondering why on earth he had volunteered. He was quite relieved when he finally reached the great door of Standard Test which was firmly shut, but even that looked twice as big as normal!

There was the small side door, and as soon as Roger walked in, he felt quite back at home again. Here there were decent lights, the shop looked just the same as in the daytime, but it was still quiet as no machines had yet started tests. There were a small group of testers studying some worksheets, and Roger went forward and introduced himself. The chief immediately welcomed him and said, "Ah good, I've got just the job for you, and led him to a test station that looked all wired up. "This is a traction motor for London Underground that the day shift have already wired up ready for a heat run tonight. Do you know what I mean?"

"Sure" said Roger, I've been doing some all last week."

"Good" said Chief "Now this is a powerful direct current motor that you have to start up gently with a rheostat. Do you understand?"

Now Roger knew the theory of starting direct current motors, and nodded his head. "We did them at college," he said. He knew the principle that the stator, the stationary outside, was energised by a field winding to turn it into a powerful magnet. Then, when you applied a small voltage to the second winding on the rotor, this would generate a current in the rotor, and the stator field acting on the current in the rotor would push the rotor winding round and cause it to revolve. The stronger the rotor current, the more torque it would develop and the faster the rotor would revolve. However, in spinning round, the rotor develops an internal counter voltage which cuts down the rotor current, so that more voltage has to be applied to the rotor.

The Tester interrupted his reverie. "The simple basic rule is that as you apply more voltage to the rotor though this rheostat," and he pointed to the controller, a large metal box with a handle on the top, "the motor speeds up. You start at notch one and slowly push the handle up to number 10 which is full speed. But you must move the controller gently, because each notch gives an extra surge of current, and you must wait till the current dies down before you move on. If you try to hurry, you will get a current overload and the supply will trip out. Secondly, when you get up to notch ten, you can now adjust the speed a little with this stator field resistance here," pointing to another controller, "and now carefully adjust to the exact speed required of 1,800 rpm. If you increase the field resistance, the magnetising field current will drop and the motor will go faster. Reducing this resistance will do the opposite, and make it go slower. Is all that clear?"

"Quite clear thanks," said Roger, "I remember that from college."

"Good" said the chief "I'll just give it a quick spin to check it all," and he proceeded to switch on the power and gently moved to notch one. The motor obediently started to rotate, and as it gathered speed so the ammeter in the rotor circuit dropped down as expected. He closed down again. "Good! that's "OK", now I'll leave it to you," and he sauntered off up a narrow stairway to a little office overlooking the test bay.

"Right," thought Roger, and after making sure his report sheets were ready and his pencil sharpened, he closed the supply switch and started. Notch one went as before, and so did notches two and three, each time the initial surge of rotor current dropping down as the motor gathered speed. "So far so good," he said to himself although he was a little surprised at the noise as the machine gathered speed. He wasn't used to a speed of 1,800 rpm. Until then he had only met 1,000 rpm. "I'll get used to it," he said between his teeth and pressed on to notch six. He stopped here as the noise was starting to frighten him, and he eased back to notch three to have a think. He just couldn't think above the noise at notch six. However, nothing seemed wrong, everything seemed as predicted except the noise! So Roger went on again gingerly to notch six. He then gritted his teeth and tried notch seven, the noise was awful, the set was shaking and he could feel the whole floor trembling beneath his feet. He just couldn't go on like this and he was about to ease back again when he found the chief of Test pushing him sideways and shouting.

"What the fuck are you playing at?" and promptly closing everything down.

The sudden cessation of noise brought a great surge of relief to Roger and he stood there shaking. "I was still trying to get up to speed," he said.

"Up to speed! you damn near had the set *flying*. What on earth have you done?"

"Nothing" said Roger feeling as miserable as if he was up before the headmaster at school. "I simply started to go through the notches like you did, and the set got faster and faster. I haven't touched any wiring or anything at all!"

"Humph! let me have a go. It was all right when I left you," and the chief switched on again and started up himself. As before, it started on notches one to three without any comment, but when he tried notch four he paused. "There's something wrong here," he said, and closed everything down. He then got out the wiring diagram, and started checking. Inside no time at all he started to swear. "The stupid bastards! The stupid, stupid bastards! Do you know what they've done?"

"No," said Roger feeling totally lost.

"They've gone and connected the field winding on the wrong side of the rheostat! As we notched up, so we took off the field winding. That would have meant infinite speed if you had gone further, but of course the set would have gone to buggery before then, and you probably with it," the chief added grimly. "Anyhow, it's not your fault," he said. "It's those bloody idiots who set this up on day shift, I'll give them hell tomorrow, we could have had a nasty accident." The chief quickly changed the one connection, tested it himself, everything went smoothly, and with an "OK Roger, over to you now" he sauntered back to his office. Several testers had gathered round at the noise, and they told Roger that they had never seen chief move so fast. He had come leaping down from the office three steps at a time.

Roger now started the tests again, and this time had no trouble getting up to notch ten, and adjusting the speed to exactly 1,800 rpm.

He pondered in his mind what speed he had reached before. He daren't think, but the noise now was nothing like the terrible din before. "What a difference just one simple connection had made!" he thought.

Sometime later, with everything running smoothly, another tester came up, checked the readings and said, "Good, that's looking fine, I expect you could do with a break after that scare?"

"But the test isn't finished yet."

The Tester laughed, "Come and join us for tea, you don't need to hover over this machine all the time, the shop is quiet enough at nights so just sit with us and keep an ear cocked on the test run. We have our own rules at night! Also, we make our own tea, after that little shock you've had, a sit down will do you good." Roger felt grateful for the understanding, and after his next set of readings he joined the little group of staff just sitting down in the proverbial circle of closed toolboxes around a gas ring in which a billy-can was coming to the boil.

One tester was unwrapping a pile of sandwiches and spreading them out on the other end of his oily toolbox. He peered at them with a frown, "Oh God!" he exclaimed, "more bloody cheese sandwiches! She gave me cheese nearly every sodding day last week. She's got no imagination."

His neighbour looked at him and snorted, "Don't, be so damn fussy. At least your good missus gives you plenty! She must think you need fattening up!"

The first tester snorted, "But there must be other things besides sodding cheese, she must think I'm a bloody mouse."

Another tester joined in "What do you suggest? Perhaps caviar and mustard? that might even get your pecker up when you got home!" They all laughed. "That's not the problem," he protested "thank you, you're no bloody help!" and he stared at his sandwiches again. He suddenly turned to Roger, "Would you care for one of these? There's twice as many here as I can eat."

Roger looked at them, they looked lovely, nice thick new bread, with a good slice of cheddar inside, industrial workers were still getting much larger cheese rations than the outside world where rationing was still in force; a world from which Roger was now feeling farther and farther away. He still retained his healthy country appetite, and he therefore accepted a large sandwich with many thanks, sank his teeth into it and sat back feeling he had truly arrived.

One of the testers suddenly started laughing, "I heard a good story from day shift this afternoon. Old Bogey Heaton was at it again!" Everyone looked up in anticipation.

"Go on" said several "Well, he went patrolling round the shop this morning, and in one corner he found a kettle on a gas ring coming up to the boil."

"So what!" someone said, "it goes on all the time." "Not any more in Standard Test," chortled the storyteller, "Apparently Bogey has had enough of it. He just stood there and watched the kettle coming to the boil without saying a word."

"Blimey!" said someone. "You can guess the rest," said the story teller, "No one would go near the kettle to own up it was their's, and the kettle came to the boil, and still the old bugger said nothing and didn't move. In the end the kettle boiled dry and the bottom melted. Then Bogey just went back to his office without saying a word to anyone!" There was a great guffaw all round. "Good job he's too old for night shift or we would be in the shit!" and they all agreed.

"Does that mean the end of private brews?" asked another. "Not a chance," someone said, "It will soon come back again, Bogey's retiring soon."

"I remember an earlier story about Bogey," said another tester. "You know how fussy he is about keeping all the gangways clean and tidy? A few years ago he was foreman in Big Shop, and he spotted a gangway one day with a load of swarf all over the place. Nasty little shavings of steel from a fitter who had been drilling some bolt-holes in a large generator shell. The fitter had gone off somewhere and left the shavings on the floor, and when Bogey looked around he could see other nearby lanes in the same mess."

"What did he say?" asked someone.

"Like today," the storyteller continued, "he didn't say a word, but went and got a broom and dustpan, and swept it up himself." When he went back an hour later, the whole floor was as clean as a whistle, you could have eaten your dinner off it"

Another tester chipped in "He's a funny bloke you know, he still rules with a rod of iron, and yet out of work he is quite a different character. He's a very religious man and is very active in his local church, everyone who has dealings with him outside says he is a very kind and gentle soul who will help anyone." The speaker turned to Roger "Bogey was in charge of you apprentices for years you know!"

"And he kept you in order," said another, "there are many tales of apprentices getting up to tricks, but for years before the war he was your absolute boss. He was very strict and exacting. Anyone late for work was immediately docked some of his pittance of a wage, and in those days, apprentices had to pay for the privilege of working here in the first place."

"I have met Mr Heaton," said Roger, "I was called to his office one day for a telling off."

"What had you been up to?" they all asked.

"It's a long story," explained Roger "and I thought it was going to be very awkward, because I had never met him before, although I had heard lots of tales about him." He paused and then explained, "I had written a poem for the apprentices magazine, everyone thought the poem was quite funny and it got accepted in the next issue."

"What was it about?" asked a tester.

"It was a skit on psalm 23 in the Bible. The first two lines went:
"The GEC is my shepherd, I need not work,
"He leadeth me to lie down besides still workers—-"
—and it went on like that as a parody of the whole psalm, and it got through the management censor. The journal went out and I forgot all about it. About three days later, our boss, Rolly, phoned me up and summoned me immediately to come and see him. I could tell by his tone there was something wrong! When I got to his office, he was in quite a stew, and told me that this Mr Heaton had been on the phone to him in a terrible rage about my poem, he had said it was not only sacrilegious, but a slur on the whole company. He had then reminded Rolly that he, Mr Heaton, had been in charge of apprentices for years before the formal ETO had been formed, and he had never had such a disgraceful episode in his time. He was so angry that he was going to

see the managing director about it." "Crikey" said one of the listeners, "when old Bogey gets annoyed, he really can let fly."

"Well, it was all a bit of a shock to me," continued Roger "and Rolly sounded almost scared for his job. He finished off his moan to me about it by saying that he had apologised profusely, and promised Mr Heaton that I would go up to his office and also make my own personal apology. So off I had to go!"

"Bully for you," said a listener, "What happened?"

"I went straight away. His office took a bit of finding, and he kept me waiting for about ten minutes outside. Then he called me in, told me to sit down in the chair opposite his desk, and sat and read through the whole text of the journal from start to finish without saying a word. His face was expressionless, and he finally turned back to my poem. He then looked up with a sigh, and said mildly, 'I don't find this at all funny.' I don't know what I managed to stammer out," said Roger, "it was some sort of apology I supposed, and he just nodded and was silent for a moment. He then explained to me how the psalm 23 was greatly loved, and had been and still was a great source of comfort all round the world to many in distress. He himself had been in sad circumstances where very sick people were near to death, and the only thing they asked him to do was to help them say the Lord's Prayer and psalm 23.' I felt awful of course," said Roger, "I must have said something, and then Mr Heaton suddenly changed his tone and asked me how my apprenticeship was going. He seemed to forget all about the journal, discussed my progress and what my ambitions were, had a few kind words of encouragement, and then I was dismissed!"

"Phew!" said a tester, "I bet you were glad to get out of there."

"Say that again," said Roger, and after a little more general chat, they all went back to work.

CHAPTER 5

"When I nod my head – hit it"

Building a large AC generator in Big Shop

Roger had so far found every new shop a quite different experience, but this next move, to "The Big Shop", beat them all. To begin with, the building was enormous, large machine tools at work one end, new generators and motors being assembled further down, apprentices and staff swarming everywhere, and two large, high crane gantries across the width of the shop. The cranes seem to be very busy; quite noisy, and in continual use. After the story of the dropped unit in the Transformer Shop, Roger viewed all cranes with some apprehension, and he now stared up at these busy giants in some trepidation. He walked into the shop carefully, mindful of many dangerous looking devices around him, stepped over a pair of overalled legs sticking out from under a half-built motor, and finally found the foreman's office.

As in all earlier shops, the office was full of grimy piles of paper and a man standing there muttering to himself angrily as he juggled with a handful of further papers. Roger coughed to attract his attention. There was no door he could knock on.

"Ah good!" said the man, a short cheerful but tough looking individual, and taking Roger's papers without a glance said straight away, "Go down to the end of the shop and give Jerry a hand, he has a load of steel sheets to bring over to the guillotines. You will need the big crane to get high enough to clear everything, it's a straightforward job, will take you both about an hour," and with that Roger realised he was expected to be on his way.

"Jigger me!" he thought "cranes already! What a start! Ah well, here we go," and with a brief, he hoped nonchalant "OK" to the foreman, he set off towards the far end of the shop where the foreman had pointed.

Roger found Jerry standing by a large pile of sheets of steel, waving his arms energetically to attract the crane. He saw Roger and smiled. "Morning son, go and get a pair of gloves from that box over there," he pointed. "You've come just in time." Roger found the box, and took out a thick pair of large leather gloves, well used and full of so much grime he could hardly bend the fingers. He then turned and saw the crane already looming down towards them with its huge hook, as big as Roger's head, swinging a foot or two from side to side as it descended. "Keep clear," said Jerry. "It will settle in a minute, old Sailor's in a hurry this morning." Roger looked up and saw the crane driver leaning out of the window of his little travelling cabin and staring down at them.

"Morning Jerry," he shouted, "how did the footy go yesterday?"

"We lost!" Jerry shouted back. "Two nil, but we blame the ref, he was bleeding useless."

"It's your own fault, no excuses, why don't you come and join a decent team!" shouted back Sailor with a grin.

"Bollocks," shouted back Jerry, and turned to Roger. "He's a bugger on a Monday morning, can't forgive me for sticking to my own club, he wants me to join his."

Roger was far too worried to listen, the big hook was almost on top of them by now, but he was still to learn what these men found most important. Jerry then turned back to Sailor and shouted up again, "We've got to get forty sheets up to the guillotines, I'm going to get this lad started, and then go up the other end to unload. I shall leave the lad here to do the slinging, keep an eye on him will you?"

"OK ,OK," shouted Sailor as the great hook came to a stop.

"Bighead!"

"Right lad," said Jerr,y "ever done any slinging before?"

"No, never," swallowed Roger doing his best to sound calm. "Well it's easy enough, you'll soon get the hang of it. This little load will be easy. First we need to get the claws, they're over here," and Roger helped him pull out two sets of chains with a large claw hook at each end. "We'll take six sheets at a time," explained Jerry, "We first have to sling the chains over the hook, and fix one set each side with the claws pushed firmly into the pile." He demonstrated, the sheets were all about ten foot by six, and Jerry used a lever to lift the sheet's edge up to insert the claws. "The main thing," said Jerry "is to space the claws so that they look balanced and evenly spaced. If not, the pile will tip when we start to lift. If that happens, you will hear plenty from Sailor. We don't call him Sailor for nothing, it's not for his looks, it's for his language." Roger did his best to grin but his mouth was too dry, somehow he managed to nod his head, and followed Jerry closely. They lowered the giant hook further to get the chains over and then he and Jerry slotted the claws in position. Jerry then stepped back and signalled for the hook to be gently lifted. "One important thing," said Jerry, "is to always tell Sailor what to do by hand signals. Shouting is too dangerous, and Sailor will take no notice."

Roger watched mesmerised as the hook gently took up the slack in the chains, and then started to take the strain. "Stand well back," shouted Jerry as the pile of clamped sheets came clear of the sheets below and swung an inch to and fro on the chains. "This is always the dangerous moment," said Jerry, "when the load first breaks free from its base. If we haven't got the hook properly over the centre of gravity of the load, it will immediately start swinging towards it. Most loads here are often much heavier than ours today, and if they swing, anything in the way gets knocked to buggery. What-ever you do, don't rush forward to steady it, just keep well out the way." Roger nodded his head, watching transfixed as their load steadily rose high in the air and started to trundle on its way over the heads of everyone working below and off to the distant far end of the shop. "Right," said Jerry, "I'm off to the other end to do the unloading, you stay here and sling the rest of the pile. Sailor will keep an eye on you," and he hurried off leaving Roger on his own.

It seemed no time at all before the crane came rumbling back, and Roger braced himself to have a go. He noted with relief that the crane hook seemed to descend more gently than before. The chains were still there hanging down, and Roger swallowed hard, and stepped forward to start. "Take your time," shouted Sailor from his cabin, and Roger felt a little relaxed by this confident and cheerful shout. Roger set to work. Everything seemed heavier now he was on his own and Roger felt grateful for his strength. He recalled the years at home where he had had plenty of lifting and tugging of heavy loads during the holidays. Also, the gloves he had on were essential, the sheets had

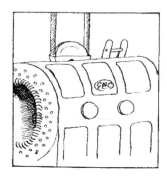

quite sharp edges, and although Roger prided himself on the toughness of his hands, lots of farm work and cricket had seen to that, but here he recognised that bare hands would not last for five minutes in a job like this. He followed all Jerry's advice carefully, and when his first load was finally lifted clear, it hardly swung sideways at all. "Good lad!" came the shout from above, and Roger watched with his heart in his mouth as his own first load disappeared over everyones' heads down the length of the shop.

After the first load Roger felt much easier, the work went more quickly and he was soon surprised to find himself saying "'goodbye"

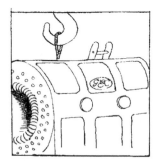

to the last pile. "I've done it" he said to himself with elation and sighed with relief.

In a few minutes Jerry came back. "Well done son," he smiled.

"Thanks," said Roger trying to sound calm "What do I do next?"

"The next thing you do is to put my bloody gloves back in the box," Jerry grinned. "I lose more gloves than hot dinners in this place." He paused and took out a battered watch. "Now that was a good job done, and now it's time for a cup of tea," and led Roger to where a tea lady was already busy pouring out the national beverage into the usual wide

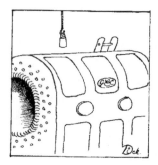

range of receptacles.

"You can't call some of these mugs at all," thought Roger, and happily sat down on a box and joined the others. The rest of the day passed with no alarms, it mainly consisted of standing behind a fitter and handing up the tools as he called for them. Picking the right size of spanner was second nature to these men, he discovered, and he was laughed at more than once when he had to hold an oily well-used spanner up to the light to read its gauge, often half-obliterated by time and usage.

At dinner back at the Hall in the evening Roger, started telling the table about his first day in Big Shop. Several had already finished their stint there, and all agreed that Big Shop had been a major step in their apprenticeship. From the tone of their talk, Roger sensed they had all enjoyed their time there, and Roger secretly hoped he would soon feel the same. He told them that his very first job had been some crane slinging work, and how he had felt very nervous.

"Oh, you'll soon get used to it," said his neighbour at the supper table. "They use the crane for everything, I think that if it old Sailor would let them, they would use a crane to hold their mug of tea!" There was laughter, and another, obviously older apprentice who they all called Jack turned to him. "You might in time, have a go at being 'King of the Crane', that will test your nerves!" he grinned, and several of them smirked with a secret knowledge.

"What do you mean?" asked Roger.

"Well," said the new speaker, "we had better not tell you here, because it's a very sore point with management, and some of these walls have ears." Roger was intrigued, "Go on, tell me more."

"No, not here," said the storyteller, "but some of us are going down the pub later, we'll tell you then if you care to join us, about eight o'clock?"

"Yes please, I'd love to," said Roger eagerly.

"Fine," came the reply, "see you then. You'll have to put your share of lolly into the pot when we start but we're not heavy drinkers, can't afford it!" and the conversation changed.

Roger felt elated, and after dinner about ten of the lads from the Hall including Roger, went down to the village pub, only two hundred yards down the road from the Hall. The bar was already fairly full, and Roger was surprised to see locals greet them with open arms like old friends.

"We come down here at least once a week," someone explained to Roger, "Jack has a good voice, and Tom gets on the piano over there and we often give them an impromptu sing-song. Jack was in the army during the war, and knows lots of the army ditties, and they love it. When we get going, everyone joins in and it goes on till closing time." Jack and Tom were part of the Hall party, and Roger noted they were already being offered free drinks by a man at the bar.

"Will we sing tonight?" asked Roger, "because I'll love to join in."

"No, not on a Monday," said his companion. "Everyone's a bit flat, but come Friday or Saturday, I expect we'll be here again. We go round a lot of pubs over the months, they all love us coming, and we all have a really good time." As they talked, drinks were being organised by their party, and everyone chipped into the pot an agreed amount, enough for about two pints each. The first conversation then, as custom demanded, was about the quality of the beer, and the general consensus was OK.

Then Jack the apprentice who had raised the subject of cranes at dinner, turned to Roger and said, "So you want to learn about the King of the Crane?"

"Yes please," said Roger and the story teller took a long drink ready to start.

"The first thing to realize," said Jack, "is that quite a few of us were in the services before we came here, and had got quite used to handling heavy loads like, for instance, getting a tank out of a ditch, so that using or handling big cranes doesn't give us any worries. In fact, we enjoy it." He stopped for another sip of his pint.

Roger joined in "Well, I felt quite nervous this morning," he admitted.

"I can imagine," said Jack. "We all do at first. Now, the 'King of the Crane' game sort of developed one night when we were on night shift in Big Shop with nothing much to do. The crane driver had been called over the road to Main Test for an hour to handle a big job," he explained. "There is only one crane driver on nights shared between the two shops as we don't need a full time driver each. Well, there were four of us on nights at the time, and no one else was around so we thought we would get up the ladder to the crane runway, and see if we could start the crane ourselves."

Roger looked amazed, "Really?" he stammered, "Yes we sure did," grinned Jack, "and inside a few minutes we had got the hang of it, and could trundle the crane to and fro."

"Someone then had the bright idea of seeing how close we could get to the end buffers by the wall at the top of the shop, you know, a sort of manoeuvering competition. We all had a try and found it quite a tricky thing to do. We then sorted out the rules for the game. We would all start the crane from the same point, about twenty feet from the end well and go at full speed towards the wall. When we thought we had gone near enough, we would slam the crane into reverse. The crane would grind to a shuddering stop, and then start going backwards. We had one of us stand on the top gangway alongside the crane track and mark with a piece of chalk the exact spot where the crane reversed. The driver who reached nearest to the wall would be acclaimed 'King of the Crane'!"

Roger was astonished. "You did that with the big crane?" he asked.

"Sure did," said someone else joining in, "a lot of us got the hang of it and it was quite a game."

Roger was dumbfounded. "But didn't anyone stop you? Didn't you do any damage? Wasn't anyone hurt?"

The party seemed highly amused at his reaction and Jack joined in again. "Oh no, we weren't that stupid, and there was no-one about who seemed to take any notice."

Roger thought for a moment trying to picture the scene, "But what about the hook?" he asked, "Wouldn't that swing around causing damage?"

"No," said Jack. "Good question, but we thought of that before we started and pulled it up tight to the top so that it was fixed. From then on," continued Jack with relish "we repeated the game on several occasions, different apprentices had a go, and to be named 'King of the Crane' became a badge of distinction." There was silence for a companionable moment while more drink was supped.

"We only had one awkward accident," Jack suddenly continued, "but I suppose it was bound to happen sooner or later. Someone, trying to beat the record, left his reversal too late, and the crane went crashing into the end stops with a mighty bang. No damage was done, but the shock of hitting the wall dislodged about twenty years of accumulated dirt from all the rafters, and a great black cloud descended to the shop floor. Unfortunately, a cleaner was just coming on shift, heard the bang and looked up to see what it was. This neatly coincided with the cloud of muck coming down, and he got absolutely covered." All the group started to laugh heartily and Roger joined in. "Well, we all thought it very funny for a short time," continued Jack "especially as the poor man stood there with his hands out in front shouting, 'I can't see, I can't see,' and started to grope around. We then realized he had a problem, and we had to climb down as quickly as we could, grab his arm, and lead him over to the medical centre where it took them over half an hour to clean him up."

"What happened next?" asked Roger.

"Not a lot," replied Jack. "We all went back to the shop, no-one else asked any questions and we just got on finishing the shift. We had to put an entry into the accident report so we simply wrote '*removing grit* from *eye*' and no one ever asked any more questions."

Another member of their party chimed in. "In the end, after we had done it several times, management got an idea something was going on and I think we have called off any more trials for the time being."

"Just as well!" thought Roger, he couldn't see himself climbing up and having a go.

The rest of the first week went well for Roger, he still had plenty of hanging about handing up tools, but at least, the fitters were friendly, and gave him some jobs like drilling and tapping holes in end plates. One nasty job was filing off the rough edges of some machined pieces, once again a job where thick gloves were essential. Steel was stubborn stuff to file, and the steel filings and general muck got everywhere. The work made Roger really sweat and he noted that this job was always given to apprentices, it was easy to see why.

Lunchtimes were always enjoyable, and a valuable source of jokes, know-how and information. One day, his table had been discussing stored energy and inertia, the subject had come up at the local technical college. Several of the student apprentices were studying there on day release, and they often all joined together at lunch to sort out common homework problems. After some general talk, and some scribbling on paper, Roger interrupted. "I can tell you a true story about inertia," he said. "I heard this from an ex-army engineer now demobbed and back at college studying for his degree. This engineer said that in Germany at the end of the war, his group visited a large factory to examine the equipment, and found the place an absolute shambles. A witness then told them that the havoc had been caused not so much by an allied bomb, but by a large flywheel that had been dislodged and came off its bearings. This flywheel was eight foot in diameter and spinning at speed when it broke loose, it fell to the steel floor, and stood there for a few seconds just spinning away and throwing out a great shower of sparks from underneath. The noise was a terrible screeching sound and the gyroscopic action kept it upright like a large spinning top. Then, as people ran for cover, it slowly started to creep forward as it got a grip on the floor, still throwing out a trail of sparks behind like a Catherine wheel, and it slowly gathered speed. It then really got moving, careering across the shop floor, flattening or climbing over everything in its way, and went straight through the brick wall at the side. It then careered across a yard at a good speed, straight through another wall into an adjacent shop where it finally fell on its side and came to rest."

"Phew! that's some story," said his neighbour, and they sat picturing the scene as they finished their meal.

During the next few weeks, Roger had a number of surprises, the first coming quite soon when a fitter he was working with suddenly asked, "Can you play draughts?"

"Why, yes, I suppose so!" Roger answered a little mystified.

"I bet you can't beat our Jamie!" the fitter continued. "He's a champion, no-one can beat him," he smirked. "You will have to try one lunchtime. He takes on everybody who comes into this shop, and he always wins."

Roger felt intrigued, it was years since he had touched a draughts board but from memory the game was very simple, and he was interested. "Well, I haven't played for years," he said, "but I don't mind having a go!"

"Right, I'll get it fixed," said the fitter, and the very next day, a little group gathered round Roger as the lunchtime hooter went. "Jamie is waiting for you today," said his mate. "Will you come?"

Roger was surprised to realise that this was an event many men liked to see happen with a newcomer, and they all trooped down together to a corner where a quite elderly man was sitting in grimy overalls on a box and just starting to eat his sandwiches.

"Put them down," said the fitter. "We've got another clever young man here challenging you to a game of draughts!".

Roger now realised he had really been put on the spot, "Well, I'm not really a challenger," he said. "I've been talked into this, but I'll have a game if you like."

Jamie just looked up at Roger. "If you like," he said, and without another word, smiled and took from his toolbox a very battered draughts board and some equally grimy draughtsmen which were so well used you could now hardly tell the black from the white.

Jamie set draughts out on the board with a practiced flourish and held out his clenched hands for Roger to choose which colour. Roger chose, it turned out to be the black, and they sat down each side of the board on boxes and started. Jamie never seemed to hesitate between moves, but whatever Roger played Jamie replied immediately with a bored expression without hardly glancing at the board. In no time at all, Roger realised he was boxed in, and whatever he did he was losing two pieces to Jamie's one. The game was soon over. "Try again!" said Jamie, speaking for the second time. "You start with white."

Once again, exactly the same pattern repeated, even though Roger felt he should have had the advantage of the first move, and Roger was soon once more admitting he was well and truly beaten. Without another word, Jamie just smiled, carefully gathered up all the pieces, put them back in his box and went back to his sandwiches.

"Told you so!" said Roger's mate. "He always wins," and with a general feeling of satisfaction and good will all round, the little crowd dispersed to their various businesses.

"Well I'm blessed," thought Roger, "that old man must know every possible move by heart," and he went off to his own lunch.

The following week, Roger was impressed by watching a very large milling machine slowly cutting a slot in a large rotor. The rotor was over twenty feet long made of solid steel, and five feet in diameter. The rotor could weigh up to forty tons. The milling machine was

slowly travelling down the length of the rotor, with a revolving cutter
chewing out a deep slot as it went along. Swarf, the sharp coils of thin
steel shavings being cut away from the slot, were falling steadily on the
floor underneath. At first, Roger was startled, he thought there was no
one in charge, but then he spotted a little, once again, quite elderly
man sitting on a high stool in well worn overalls and busy reading a
grimy newspaper. Roger turned to the fitter he was with. "Look at
that!" he said. "That man is the only one near that enormous job, and
he's not taking a bit of notice, he's reading a newspaper!"

The fitter laughed, "That old man is one of our best machinist on
the shop floor, he'll be retiring next year, and we don't know what we
shall do without him, he gets all these very expensive jobs."

Roger sounded unbelieving, "but he's not even looking at it!"

"He may not be watching it" answered the fitter, "but his ears are
tuned to it, and the slightest change of sound and he will be off that
stool like a shot." The fitter continue. "Once the tool setter has set the
next slot position and got the machine started, there's nothing else to
do for over an hour, they can't change anything once the slot has
started. It's a two man job, and their skill is in setting the cutter
absolutely accurately in the first place. If the slot is more than a few

thousandths of an inch out of position, the whole rotor job will be ruined." The fitter carried on with pride in his voice. "When that rotor is finished, with all the copper windings slotted in and locked down, the rotor will spend years in service spinning at three thousand rpm, that's fifty revolutions per second. Any unbalance at that speed will cause a build-up of oscillations and it might end up ruined."

"Never!" exclaimed Roger staring at in awe.

"Oh yes it can" the fitter assured him, "vibration could cause the thin oil film in the bearing to break down, then the rotor would seize up, the pedestal bearing could be torn from its foundations, and just about anything could happen, several have done that over the years." They both stood watching for a few minutes. Roger found himself more than impressed, he felt quite humbled by the skill and years of experience he was watching.

That evening, Roger mentioned his views back at the Hall and Jack agreed with him. "I often feel the same," he said. "The point is that the older generation of workers did not have any opportunity to advance their education, there were no such things as scholarships to Grammar schools between the wars, if you were born into a working class family around here, that's where you stayed." Roger nodded in understanding he was a scholarship boy himself. Jack then continued, "I have met quite a few very clever men here in overalls, who nowadays would be going to grammar school, and on to top jobs like doctors or lawyers. They are mostly the older men, doing the most skilled jobs, and when they retire, I think the shop floors will be a lot worse off." Jack gave a wry smile, "Ah well, I suppose that's progress for you," he said with a grin.

"There's nothing dangerous 'ere as long as you keep yer 'ead"

A further task, that Roger found quite unnerving, was to assist with fitting an end bell on to a rotor. The end bells are cylinders of steel which contain the copper windings where they project at the ends of the rotor body. The bells are only supported by the ends of the rotor teeth where they have to be a very tight fit. They are preheated and then eased over the end windings and finally given a slight turn to lock into the rotor teeth. The task was delicate, and Roger found the practice was to hang a large thick slab of steel on to the crane by a length of rope, and use it as a battering ram. One fitter would then hold a second bar against the end bell at a strategic spot, and tell the other fitter to swing the battering ram and hit the end of the bar he was holding. Roger once again watched mesmerised as repeated swings were made, the one holding the bar against the end bell, and the other hitting the other end of the bar with a solid thump. Despite the first fitter continually changing his bar position to another point of contact, between them they always made a direct contact on the new bar position. Roger had to join in pulling the battering ram back for the next blow which needed a strong pull, the battering ram was heavy. At every swing, Roger's heart was continually in his mouth in case the next swing missed the bar the other fitter was holding, a miss would have smashed into his fingers. He need not have worried, he soon realised the two men had total confidence in each other, swung the heavy battering ram with just the occasional invective, and the job went smoothly without any hesitation or semblance of an error.

When the first wet day came, Roger

"Actually I think the boss is cracked."

experienced a time-honoured ritual in Big Shop that considerably improved his education of the fair sex. The front end of the shop happened to be a short cut through to both the typing pool and the office block and, on a wet day, the office girls coming to work used to walk through the shop floor to escape the rain. Office hours started an hour after the works, so everybody on the shop floor was well into their work before the girls would come trooping through. On the first day this happened, Roger was assisting a fitter working underneath a motor right by the short cut route, when a very smart girl in her early twenties came mincing past, having already folded up her brolly and showing a very handsome pair of legs and wearing a short skirt. The fitter was laying on his back on the floor and half into the gangway. Roger just looked at this vision in a sort of dumb admiration and moved over to let her pass, but not so his mate. As the girl gingerly stepped over him, his mate stared up at her with no embarrassment, and said in a loud voice that carried all round the shop, "Ello Ducks! 'Ow's your old gristle gripper this morning?" Many around started to hoot with laughter, and Roger felt himself curling up inside with embarrassment. His astonishment was complete when the girl instead of looking at all put out, just joined in the laughter and went on her way. Roger could see she actually seemed pleased by the attention, and went on her way with a slight swagger!

A second incident very soon after that caused merriment one afternoon. A fitter in the same part of the shop came to work with a magazine photograph of a naked man where the emphasis in the picture was on the man's very prominent genitalia. "I'm going to have some fun with this," he promised everybody, and kept it hidden until after lunch. When the first girl came through the shop after lunch, he approached her, holding the photograph covered, and said to her innocently. "Would you like to see a picture of my baby boy?" Roger held his breath and could see nothing but trouble coming, he felt himself blushing in anticipation.

"If you like," said the girl innocently, and the fitter held the picture up to her. The girl stared at it for what seemed like ages, and then broke into a grin, "You dirty old man!" she said and ran off laughing, the shop floor to a man laughing at the same time.

To complete Roger's amazement, during the rest of the afternoon, there was a steady succession of girls from all over the place, coming in and asking if they could see "that picture of the man's baby boy?" The fitter obliged of course, and the joke kept repeating, Roger noted that there was not one visitor who seemed at all upset, only thoroughly amused! "Well, I'll go to Jericho," he thought, "what next?"

Roger related the episodes with the girls to his group of friends at the Hall, Jack was very amused. "I bet they all thoroughly enjoyed the jokes," laughed Jack. "Nothing could upset them, there's plenty of that sort of fun goes on all the time, it's only human nature when you are all working together."

"I suppose I'm still a bit naïve," smiled Roger, "although come to think of it, we did have our moments back on the nurseries. We had two sisters working for us, who we knew came from a poor family, and yet they suddenly started coming to work looking very prosperous and wearing fur coats. It coincided with the arrival of the first batch of American soldiers near the end of the war. It didn't need an Einstein to guess what they were up to, but our mum in her innocence started grumbling about it. "I can't see how those girls can afford fur coats," she said, "they must have more money than we know."

My Dad, always ready with a quip said, "It's easy, they got them wholesale." Everyone in the packing shed roared with laughter including me and my brother, but not my poor old mum, who couldn't see the joke.

"Wholesale or not!" she said angrily. "Those coats are expensive, and how can they get them wholesale when we have to pay full prices for everything!" The extra shrieks of laughter really confused Mum who was near to losing her temper until someone explained the joke.

"Can't you see," old Percy said slowly with relish in his voice "they're selling their hole!—hole sale." Poor old mum, she was so embarrassed she didn't know what to say and moaned at Dad all the evening when we got home for saying such things in front of her children.

Jack had a good laugh at the tale and changed the subject. "By the way, have you thought of going on nights in Big Shop?" he suddenly asked. "They are a grand bunch there, not many of them, but you'll certainly learn a lot, including some good stories too." Now Roger, on reflection, had really enjoyed his other night shift work in Standard Test, and so once again, he took Jack's advice, and had himself transferred to night shift the following week.

It was now wintertime, but Roger felt again the same mystery of an almost silent works when he cycled in, but he now felt at home from the start and joined in the work with a will. One irritant he found was a large sliding door at the far end of the shop, which seemed to be constantly in use. It had one snag, it was a bit worn and leaky, which in the winter was a ripe source of drafts. Many times after it was used during the night, it was never properly closed, and any fitters near it would burst into a tirade of really descriptive bad language. "At least there are no women on nights" thought Roger, and he always managed to get the job of closing the door properly. They use to hang notices on the door, some sarcastic and others more belligerent like "SLAM IT DAMN IT", but no one seemed to take any notice, It was a heavy door, and Roger got to really dislike it. On the bright side, however, was the comfortable corner where they all gathered for their evening sandwiches. The ritual was the same as Roger had found in Standard Test in his last post. There was the same good humour and relaxed atmosphere, and a great deal of gossip. They also had a useful gas ring on which they was brewed their own tea, there was no tea lady on nights, and the ring usually stayed burning all night to make the gossip corner comfortably snug whatever the temperature and drafts around the shop.

There was a second apprentice on nights with Roger, and during the course of the next two weeks they both caused minor accidents, and both accidents concerned crane usage. Roger's happened first, and occurred when two fitters he was working with started to hoist up a large motor for transport to Main Test. They had just finished fitting some end guards, and Roger was feeling very pleased as they had let him drill and tap the holes in the body. He had managed the job accurately, the guards had been bolted on sweetly, and the fitters had complimented him. The giant crane was almost ready to lift and the fitters were just finishing adjustments to the hoisting cables when one of the fitters suddenly joked, "The lad seems to know what to do when he's dealing with *holes*," and they all started to laugh. It was the sort of corny joke that was quite often came up in some shape or other, and Roger in time-honoured fashion stuck two fingers in the air at the joker. This was a bad mistake as the crane driver, watching them closely from above, immediately started to lift. He stopped almost immediately as the two fitters leapt back in alarm shouting loud abuse, and the crane driver cut off power, and climbed down to give them all an earful. Roger felt dreadful. He well knew the crane always and only responded to hand signals; it had been a lesson on his first day in the shop! At least, no one was hurt, but as Roger realised all too clearly, it could have been a very nasty accident if the men had still been handling the slings; the slings were half-inch thick steel cables and would have ripped their fingers off! It was a lesson, and he never made the same mistake again.

The second incident concerned Roger's mate, who was entrusted one day with slinging a motor generator set on his own and getting it transported to another part of the shop. It was not a particularly large unit, and the lad set about calling the crane, and fitted on the hoisting cables with great confidence. Soon the cables were in position, and the lad lifted the hook up a little way very gently to take up the slack in the cables in order to have a last check. Everything looked fine, the lad gave a sigh of relief, and signalled to the crane driver to lift away. The giant hook obediently started upwards and the cables became tight. Then a strange thing happened, there was a loud sort of "ping" noise, followed by a whizzing sound and a clatter at the far end of the shop. The crane stopped immediately and started to come down again, but not before a second "ping" occurred followed by the same whizzing and clatter somewhere else.

The poor lad realised in a flash what was happening He had forgotten to take out the four half-inch bolts that were bolting the unit to the shop floor! The noise had attracted everyone's attention and two fitters near the far end of the shop had ducked for cover at the whizzing noise. Inspection showed that as the crane pulled, the heads of two of the bolts had been snapped clean off and flown away like bullets. Everyone gathered round and stared at the shiny stumps of the bolts, and nodded sagely at the force of the crane. Once again, no one was hurt, and the incident was passed with a solemn warning to the lad, but it was considered the sort of mistake that no one would ever make twice.

On evening at snack time, one of the fitters turned to Roger. "A dicky-bird tells me that you were a right mad sod during the war?"

"Not exactly," said Roger laughing, "but someone's been telling you about our souvenir hunting on the South Downs. What I said was all absolutely true," sighed Roger, "and I often think back now and sigh for the fun and excitement we had."

"But gathering live ammo and bringing it home sounds like suicide to me," pursued his questioner. "Surely you were stopped by some-one?"

"No, never that I can remember," said Roger. "There was a war on, and most of the time we were left to ourselves. There were plenty of incidents to keep the few policemen we had busy without bothering about us, we got a few lectures at school, and that was about all."

Some-one else joined in, "But some boys were killed, didn't you say?"

"Yes they were, and several were maimed," agreed Roger, "but, thank goodness, our gang never had any terrible accidents like that. Perhaps we were a bit more careful, or knew a bit more than some."

"Didn't you have any near misses?"

"Well, there were a couple I can remember" answered Roger thinking back to those golden days "One day, on a lovely hot summers' day, our gang was up on the Downs looking for slow-worms. We used to catch them and take them to school or to cricket. They often caused panic, because they look just like adders and they would rear up with their forked tongue shooting out and scare the pants off those who don't know them. We could tell the difference because the adders have a dark V mark at the back of the head otherwise they look just the same. We leave the adders well alone."

"You young buggers," a listener said.

"We make our own fun in the country," laughed Roger. "Well, on this day we were walking along, looking at the edge of the path closely, when someone spotted a nice clean bomb laying on the side, we didn't know what it was, but the general opinion was that it was a three inch mortar bomb. It was absolutely clean and shiny never been fired or anything, and we didn't know what to do with it. Then someone had a good idea. 'I know what,' he said, 'let's build a sort of tent of sticks over it, put a big stone on the top, tie a string to the sticks and take cover over there in the ditch. Then we can pull the string, drop the weight on the bomb, and see if it will go off.' We all thought this was a splendid idea. We found the string, there was plenty laying around those days, and we proceeded to make a flimsy tent of sticks around the bomb, being very careful not to touch it, and then we were ready to balance a nice big stone on top. Guess what happened," said Roger pausing, and looked around at his rapt audience.

"Go on then, I just can't imagine it you daft devils!" they said.

"Well, we had the string in place and were trying to balance the big stone on the top of the tent of sticks, when suddenly the whole pile, including the stone, collapsed on top of the bomb — and nothing at all happened."

"You jammy sods!" someone said. "Perhaps we were" continued Roger happily, "but by then several of us were getting windy, none of wanted to touch the pile again, so we just went home and left it there." Roger by now was thoroughly enjoying his reminiscences.

"There was another incident," Roger continued "When we found a tin full of little copper discs that looked like biggish pills with a small flange each side, no one knew quite what they were, but the general opinion was that it was a tin full of percussion caps. Well, to check this, my brother placed one on the concrete path near our kitchen door, and hit it with the back of the chopper. It took several blows but it didn't respond, but just took on a rather sad shape, so we were about to give up when my brother tried one last real mighty whack, and that did it. There was a large bang and the chopper flew out of his hand, over his head and landed several feet down the path. He was using the back of the chopper, so the blade was upper-most and it flew past his face, missing by inches. He said he felt the wind of it. At least now we knew what they were, and we set off further ones later with more careful contraptions. The most successful was a heavy wooden dart with a nail on the front over which you could clip one of the detonators. When thrown towards people it landed with a most satisfying bang."

It was time to return to work, but Roger reminded himself that one night he would tell them his tale about the Heinkel.

CHAPTER 6

"What happened then?"

A completed rotor ready for overspeed testing

Roger's next logical move was to Main Test, where all large machines were tested before dispatch. He found the atmosphere was similar to the bustle in Standard Test, but now everything was much larger and more complicated. He quickly learned a useful lesson that he used many times in the future. As previously, one of his first jobs was to help wire up a large machine for testing, and as in Standard Test, it was just the same scramble to find appropriate cables, nuts and bolts, only now everything was on a larger scale. On the first job, he was in doubt as to the thickness of cable to collect, and this time when he asked, a senior tester said. "Work on the rough guide of one thousand amps per square inch of cross section."

This guideline never let Roger down, and later in life, if he was discussing any electrical matters with any pretentious engineers, he would pick up some object such as a convenient stick and say, "If this was made of copper, how many amps could you pass through it?" Roger had a lot of fun with this question, even sometimes among so called technical experts who proved to have more talk than practical electricity knowledge.

Within the first week in the shop, he was sent up to the Instrument Room to collect a special ammeter. This room was a long ramshackle office up a flight of stairs with a good overview of all test area. Several skilled instrument makers were busy here on the usual chore of repairing delicate instruments that had suffered accidents such as being incorrectly used, or simply dropped. There were probably over one hundred meters of one sort or another in constant use in both Standard and Main Tests, and there was always a steady stream of repairs needed, coupled with a usual shortage of units fit for use. Roger entered the Instrument Room and was greeted with open arms. The special meter he had been sent to collect was ready, but before he could leave, they pressed him into trying the "Lung Testing Machine."

"Yers, – I've known him since 'e was so 'igh."

Roger was intrigued. "What do you mean?" he asked and an instrument maker went to a cupboard, fished out a strange looking device and showed it to him with pride.

"Everyone has a go at this," he said, "It won't take a minute. It works like this," and he held up the home-made looking contraption for closer inspection. It was made of strong cardboard, with a mounted propeller at one end, and a counter connected next to it, and had all the signs of plenty of use. "All you have to do," he explained, "is to rest your chin just here, shut your eyes tight and blow the propeller round with the biggest breath you can muster." He then proceeded to do this, the propeller whizzed round, and the counter reached 265 before he stopped for another breath. His two mates gathered round and commented favourably on his score. "That's not bad today," the demonstrator said "especially after the beer I had last night," and holding the device up to Roger he said "Here, have a go! and see what you can do. You are a young man, and I expect you can beat that," and he set the counter back to zero

Roger took the machine, he was pretty certain he could do better, and the tester helped him to settle his chin in the correct position. "That's it," he said. "That's just right, now have a good blow." Roger filled his lungs to capacity and blew with all his might and he heard the propeller whizzing but it only sounded half the speed of the tester. He also felt some queer prickling on his face, and when he opened his eyes they started smarting. He looked at the counter — only 112! He was very disappointed but then a tester said. "What's wrong with your face?" and held up a mirror. Roger's face was covered in soot and half the test staff on the floor below were watching through the long window in great glee. "Oh dear," said the tester apologetically, "you didn't put your finger over this hole," and he pointed to a hole in the front of the box quite cunningly concealed. Roger forced a laugh, he had really been caught this time, and he had to disappear in some confusion to get himself cleaned up. He found that the soot was all over his face and hair, and was not that easy to get off. Roger stood in the wash room and just didn't know really whether to laugh, cry, or simply swear!

Subsequently, Roger re-visited the instrument room, and examined the "Lung Tester," it was indeed a wonderful contraption, with a soot reservoir inside and so constructed that as one blew, the stream of breath was re-directed to blow the soot all over the innocent's face. If the demonstrator held his little finger over the little soot-hole, that path was stopped, and all was serene! Roger's only consolation was to learn that nine out of ten apprentices fell for the trap.

A few weeks later Roger had a salutary lesson that he never forgot. A large complicated motor generator set had been assembled, and fully wired up by the night shift, and was now ready for the day shift to start testing. Roger was assigned to this job and told to report to a Mr George Brand. Roger had already heard of George, a very practical engineer who was actually on the Outside Erection staff, but often came into the works to take important tests himself. He always wanted to make absolutely sure of important new jobs before he took them on to the customer's premises. He had a reputation for very straight dealing, no time for idiots, and like many, possessed of a rich vocabulary when the occasion demanded. On this occasion George cursorily checked all the connections prepared for them by the night shift, they looked correct, and he stationed Roger at the end of the shaft with a tachometer to check the speed as the set was run up to speed This set was designed to run at eighteen hundred rpm, a speed at which Roger was by now quite comfortable to stand next to. The tachometer is a small hand held speed measuring device that you hold against the end of the revolving shaft where it fits into a central small conical recess. "Are you ready?" called George.

"Yes," shouted Roger, and bent down and carefully pressed the tacho' against the shaft. George started to close all the switches. There was almost immediately a mighty bang, a loud hissing noise, flames and sparks seemed to be flying everywhere, and Roger, to his great personal discredit, found himself, like a gazelle, leaping over a number of cables and various obstacles, some quite high, until he found himself in safety near the main door.

He then looked back, and could see a cloud of smoke around the generator they were testing, with George's head visible above the smoke. He was still at his post, but swearing like a trooper, and calmly closing everything down in an orderly fashion. In a short time, the smoke cleared and all was quiet except for George letting rip in his choicest language. "Some stupid bastard," he shouted to Roger "has pinched one of our meters and left the connecting voltage leads lying on the floor, look at that!" and he pointed to where two cables lying on the steel floor had melted and the remains were still smouldering fitfully.

"Sorry I panicked," said Roger "I just didn't think, I don't remember anything until I found myself by the door!"

"Don't worry lad," said George laughing, "When you've been around as long as me these things become second nature. But I'm going to find the crazy bastard who lifted our voltmeter, and I'll have his guts for garters!"

A few days later, Roger was puzzled by a loud whining noise that seemed to be coming from below the floor. It was loud enough to make ordinary speech quite difficult. "What's that noise?" he shouted to George. "Its coming from down there", shouted back George pointing to the floor near one end of Test. "They are doing the final over-speed tests on a new rotor, it's down there in the over-speed pit with those large slabs of concrete on top." Roger could now identify the site, the noise was coming from below a set of tightly fitting concrete slabs set into the Test Room floor, with a complicated panel of test instruments on the shop floor nearby. Several senior engineers were staring intently at instruments and oblivious to anything else in this world. After a few minutes, one of them nodded to his neighbour. There was a visible sign of relief all round the group and the chief of test adjusted a controller. The high pitched whine started to drop in pitch as the speed reduced, and there were signs of satisfaction all round. "That's good!" said George now in a normal voice. "The rotor has been accepted by the consulting engineers, which means it can be released to go to the new power station. The running speed in service will be three thousand rpm to supply the grid at fifty cycles per second, but we have to prove to the consultants that the rotor can actually stay in one piece at a regulation ten per cent over-speed. It's always a very tricky moment after we've spent a year making it."

"Does it ever go wrong?" asked Roger. "What do you mean by 'stay in one piece?'"

"Well," said George, in a matter-of-fact voice, "you must realise that even steel has limits, and all these very large generators are designed quite close to the limits of their materials."

"Have you ever had one fly to pieces?" asked Roger sounding rather incredulous.

"No, thank goodness, but one of our competitor's rotors did two years ago."

"You're joking!" said Roger.

"I'm certainly not," smiled George. "Why do you think we do these tests in an underground pit? This competitor's rotor simply exploded, and their over-speed pit and the meters were severely damaged. We found ourselves testing all their large rotors for them for the next nine months."

"Why did you help them if they are competitors?" asked Roger.

"Of course we did," said George sounding very surprised, "Once you get away from the moneybags, you will find us engineers always help each other all the time. On nearly all big jobs there will be several Companies involved, and there is never any 'us and them' attitude on site. Life is too bloody short!"

The rotor noise had settled to a quiet hum, and Roger saw several of the test staff disappear down a ladder that led into the pit. "It's quite safe now," said George with a grin. "You can go down yourself if your nerves are strong enough." Roger felt frightened at the prospect, but obviously it must be safe. He somehow felt that George was daring him after the fiasco of his flight to the door the week before.

"Sure," he said, "I would love to."

"Leave it with me then," said Roger, "I'll have to get permission first," and he sauntered over to the chief of test who was still reading the meters near the test pit and jotting down numbers. He soon came back, "It's okay. Chief says they like all senior apprentices to do it once. They are just finishing their visual inspection, but then it will be running at three thousand rpm for the next hour, so you can go down in your own time, but I have to tell you to be extremely careful, of course, and keep to the side wall of the pit as far away from the rotor as you can."

"Of course," stammered Roger and a little later with his heart in his mouth, he was given the all clear and down the ladder he cautiously went.

The first thing that hit Roger when he reached the bottom of the ladder was the incredible noise. Up above, it had sounded a reassuring hum, but down here, in the pit, Roger felt as though all hell had been let loose. The noise was mainly the wind noise of the rotor flashing round at its fifty revolutions per second with a driving motor at the end, and the whole pit seem to be one throbbing and pulsing entity to this great whirling mass of steel and copper. It simply looked like a great twenty-five feet long, five foot diameter mass of noisy whizzing blur.

The whole floor was vibrating with the noise and Roger felt totally disoriented for a few moments. He could see that the inspection path down the side of the pit wasn't very wide at all, it left only an arm's width between the concrete wall and the mass of whirring steel. For a minute he didn't know what to do, he couldn't think clearly with all the noise. He just didn't know whether to go back up the ladder, or go forward and walk down past the side of the roaring monster. In the end, he summoned up the rest of his courage, stepped off the ladder, and started walking gingerly down the side of the pit. The noise now seemed to shriek in his ears as it came off the monster into one ear, and bounced back off the wall into the other. The floor, the walls, and even his own body and teeth all seemed to be vibrating with this dreadful noise. "Boy oh boy," he thought, "I don't need advice to stay near this wall." He felt himself wishing he could sink into it!

Roger persevered however, he just could not face George again unless he did, and so he gingerly walked along the side of the monster, with one hand touching the vibrating wall all the time. It seemed to reassure him somehow. Finally, his trial mercifully came to an end as he finished the walk and unsteadily climbed up the escape ladder at the far end.

George was waiting for him as he came out. "Well done lad," he said, "now let's get back to work." No more was said at the time, but Roger looked back on that experience for a long time, and pondered how little the average man in the street appreciated the immense forces that engineers everywhere had daily harnessed for their benefit.

The next day brought some light relief. When he arrived he found a group of the day staff holding their sides with laughter at a story being told them by one of the night shift. The centre of the hilarity was the chief of the night shift staff himself who was explaining what had happened. The chief had not gone home, but stayed over to report the incident himself to chief of test as he guessed there would be trouble coming. "What's the joke?" asked Roger, and the tester repeated his story to several newcomers who also gathered round.

"Roger" he said "you know that test on the new extraction pump that you prepared for us yesterday?"

"Yes" said Roger cautiously. He remembered it well. Main Test had occasional trouble with water seeping into the over-speed pit from the canal, Main Test was situated in a building that ran alongside the canal bank, and about once a week they had to pump out any seepage into the pit before tests. The extraction pump was old, and the general opinion was that it would soon give up the ghost. In anticipation, a brand new, more powerful pump had just been delivered, and as for everything in Main Test, it was decreed that it should have a thorough test. Accordingly, Roger and a team had assembled the testing arrangements that afternoon ready for the night shift. The chief of test himself had supervised the set-up, which consisted of a hose pipe into the canal sucking water out, this was fed to the new pump, with a discharge pipe lifted high and fed back through a high window back into the canal.

"This will give sufficient head of water to properly load the new pump" the chief had explained, "and I want it to be run over-night for four hours to really give it a good belting, full documentation of the test as usual please, we can't have anything here that is not one hundred per cent reliable."

The team including Roger had spent the afternoon assembling everything as instructed, and had given the pump a quick trial run to check everything was perfect. The only slight problem had been the nuisance of going out of Main Test, through the canal gate and checking that the discharge pipe fed back cleanly into the canal water. The first pipe did not reach far enough and the discharge water had spewed all over the canal path. Several visits outside were needed before a longer pipe was adjusted, supported by a stick which at last gave a satisfactory output flow straight back into the canal.

"What went wrong?" asked Roger. "We gave it a quick trial spin before we left, and it was all working perfectly."

"I'll tell you what went wrong," said the story-teller starting to laugh again. "We started the test at about eight o'clock, and everything went like a charm for a couple of hours until we heard a furious pounding on the canal gate which by that time of night was locked. We got the keys, opened the gate with a man outside hammering at it all the time. The man was a bargee, and he was absolutely beside himself with rage. At first we couldn't understand a word he said but he was pointing furiously at the canal. We looked, and there was his barge, right underneath our discharge pipe, full to the brim with water and sunk to the bottom. The poor man had arrived with his barge in the evening, unwittingly moored it accidentally, but very neatly, right underneath our vent pipe! He had then gone off for the evening to meet up with his mates and had come back to find a very wet bed!"

George had been listening with them, and joined in the repeated laughter. "You never know in our job what's going to pop up and hit you next," he said shaking his head, "but this one will take a lot of beating!"

"The poor bargee's sleeping quarters, and his little stove at the end of the barge, were of course under the water," said the story teller, "and there was absolutely nothing we could do about it at the time except apologise."

"I'm sure that was a great help!" grinned George.

"Not a lot, but after five minutes extremely bad language in broad Brummie, most of which we couldn't even understand, he stormed off back to his mates, promising blue bloody murder to the firm when he came back in the morning."

Roger heard later that it had needed a canal rescue operation and lots of negotiations with the company before the incident was put to rest.

Once again, Roger volunteered for night shift and soon found himself back in the comfortable atmosphere of a quiet, still factory. Work went on as before, but with more time, more relaxation, and more responsibility. The first useful practice he discovered was how to economise on the work needed to record and document a four hour heat run. According to the official record, the final test report would indicate that at half-hour intervals, the tester had carefully written down the various temperature readings and key electrical parameters, and then, at the end of the test, had plotted graphs to show how these figures had changed with time. However, Roger soon found that the standard practice on night shift was to take a couple of early readings, perhaps one more at half time, and two at the end when the temperatures had all settled. From these the intermediate readings could be deduced, and the official report forms completed using nice smooth freehand curves to fill in all the missing readings. Not only did this save a lot of time and legwork, but looked much neater. It was probably just as technically accurate, and resulted in a far more professional looking report at the end of the study.

This unofficial practice on night shift enabled work to be minimised and yet still to get through the work. The main reason however was the priceless advantage that it left time for more sociable activities. There was always time for discussion on a wide variety of topics, Roger discovered that the staff seemed very well versed on many subjects, and animated talks frequently extended the generous snack break periods. Also, on Friday evenings, after collecting their week's pay packets, a serious pontoon school would develop later in the night. Roger watched fascinated for several weeks, and eventually yielded to repeated invitations and joined in. The stakes were never very high, and Roger found that after losing a few bob each week at the start, he soon got into the swing and held his own. "I'm learning more here than I ever did at college," he mused happily.

One evening the topic of the war experiences developed. Many of the testers had been in the factory all through the war and could tell many tales. Two of them recalled with great affection a Chinaman fitter named Tommy Koh, who had been drafted into the factory to help with war work. "He was a really likeable little chap," recalled the first storyteller, "and he was so anxious to fit in and please us all that it was almost embarrassing. His English wasn't at all bad, and he wanted to take his share in everything." The story teller took a sip of his tea. "We all had to do our turn at night-time fire watching, as Jerry was always dropping incendiary bombs all over the place, and factories such as ours were fairly regular targets of course."

"I know," interrupted Roger. "Back in Sussex we could hear the planes coming over in droves to attack south coast targets. The steady 'throb-throb-throb' of their engines as they came over seemed to go on for ages some nights, we used to fall asleep listening, but our poor old mum just lay there worrying. If the air raid sirens had sounded, me, my brother and sister together with mum all went together downstairs into the Morrison shelter," explained Roger.

"Morrison shelter! what was that?" asked one tester who admitted he hadn't been in England during the war years.

"They were great," explained Roger. "They were the size of a full sized table tennis table, made of thick steel with strong wire mesh sides you clipped on. It was assembled in our ground floor back room. They were a government issue, and were considered strong enough to support the ruins in case a bomb caused the house to collapse. Air raid wardens kept a map of where your Morrison was, so they would know where to dig you out if you were hit. "Bugger me," said the tester, "what a time!"

"Well, as I was saying," said the first storyteller, "this Chinaman, Tommy Koh, insisted on doing his share and joining us on fire-watching duty. When we all assembled that first night, he became very worried because he didn't have a steel helmet like the rest of us. We assured him it didn't matter, but he insisted, so someone went and borrowed one of his own mate's off the shelf. 'Here, try this,' he said, and our Tommy put it on. It was a bit too big for him," continued the story teller, "but it was the best we could do, and we told him to take care of it as it would have to go back to its owner at the end of the shift. He put it on and then what do you think?" He stopped and asked his audience, and the other story tellers who had been there started to chuckle again at the memory.

"Go on then, tell us!" someone said.

"Well, our friend then started to worry whether it would be strong enough, and he wanted a check, and he picked up a sizeable bar of wood, gave it to me, and asked me to stand on the table and hit him over the head with it for a test. "Hit me really hard," he asked in his best English. Well!" he paused, and looked around grinning "I did just that, and he fell senseless, pole-axed to the floor."

"He wants to be an engineer!"

There were hoots of laughter from everyone in the room. They could all picture the scene, what an absolutely crazy idea all round! After a few minutes the second storyteller took up the tale. "We were stunned of course, poor Tommy Koh lay there as white as a sheet, and we were just about starting to panic as to what to do, when he began to come round."

"Was I relieved," said the first storyteller, "he must have been as tough as old boots, for within a few minutes he was sitting up shaking his head and assuring us he was quite all right. He refused to go to the Medical Centre, just had a mug of tea that someone produced, and announced he was ready to start his patrol."

The second story-teller then continued, "I was with him on the rounds that night, and all he kept fretting about was the bloody dent in the helmet!" and amid further merriment the night shift dispersed and got ready to pack up and go home.

On another evening snack break, when all the tests were running along comfortably without needing anyone to hover over them, Roger was pressed to tell them more about his days in the war. The tester who had not been in the country during the war was always asking questions.

"Where was your father during the war? Why didn't he stop you collecting live ammunition and running wild over the army exercise grounds like you described?" he asked.

"He would have had a job" said Roger cheerfully. "He was in the Navy over in the Far East, and in any case ever since I can remember, even before the war, our parents were quite used to us running around freely, either to play on the village green, which was just outside our house, or our gang would run up 'Hill Barn lane' and run around on the South Downs. Come to think of it," mused Roger "we used to run around for miles, we never walked. No one bothered us and we always came back home as soon as we felt hungry. None of us had watches, we simply judged the time by the sun. Yes, they were good days!" and Roger went into a reflective mood. He could see the Downs in front of him, bathed in the hot sunlight, and he and his pals all running along for the sheer fun of it until they flopped down exhausted on the springy turf to get their wind back and then maybe a spot of wrestling.

"But wartime was different" persisted his questioner.

"Well, funnily enough, us lads really didn't find anything very different, in fact it was all an adventure for us, and we quite enjoyed it really."

"Weren't you ever afraid?", he was asked.

"No, never that I can remember," Roger answered. "Silly really. We knew we would win the war because dad had told us so when he was called up." He paused for a minute, "Our mum used to get afraid at times though! One time I remember was during the 'Battle of Britain', we were on the village green trying to sort out who was who in a dogfight high above us, when we saw a parachute descending with a man dangling underneath. We rushed in and called our mum to come and see. Many others were gathering as well and we watched fascinated as the parachute slowly drifted down, and for a time we thought it would land near where we stood. However, the parachute slowly drifted across and finally landed over a mile away where the Home Guard was waiting. The man turned out to be a German fighter pilot. For weeks after that our mum was in a right tizzy as to what she would have done if he had landed in our own back garden! She had that on her mind for weeks, and the more all the neighbours laughed at her and told her not to be silly, the more she became convinced that it was only a matter of time before she would get a German pilot knocking on her own back door."

"Poor woman," said the listener, "she must have had a hard time!"

"I suppose so up to a point," Roger conceded, "but we were always doing our best to make her laugh, and she used to get letters from dad now and again. We all sat and read together and they always cheered her up."

"But your mother was probably much more worried than she let on to you boys" said his listener.

"I don't recall it" said Roger thoughtfully, "although we all used to gather round the wireless set at 6 o'clock to hear the news. That became a ritual." Roger laughed "We even had a laugh about that! There was this old lady living near us who always came in to listen to our wireless and she sat side by side with my mother, and they both listened in absolute silence to every word until the news was finished. The dear old lady, a Mrs. Wagstaff, said she would not listen to her wireless at home because it belonged to her son and it didn't tell the truth" They all started to laugh.

"Poor old soul! I can believe her thinking like that!" said a listener, "but she probably came to you for the company as much as the news."

"Were there many parachutists bailing out?" pursued his listener, who admitted that he was absolutely fascinated by these war stories. He had been in a reserved occupation in South Africa during the war, and just had no idea what it had been like in England.

"Not many had so-called fun like young Roger here," another listener said. "Most of us were either called up, or working here waiting to be bloody blown up."

"Well we were still very young," apologised Roger, "I don't suppose we would do these things now, but I'm telling you, at the time it was all very exciting."

"Exciting!" said a listener. "You are a lucky bugger to still be alive!"

"Maybe you're right," conceded Roger changing the subject, "but talking about parachutists, we picked up a lot of rumours and good stories about them from the general hearsay. One I liked was of a German pilot who landed in a field where the farmer had just finished gathering up wheat with the combined harvester. The farmer was afraid the German would run off, so while the poor pilot was still in a state of shock, the farmer pulled the lad's boots off, and then took his time to go and phone the police. It was a brilliant idea," laughed Roger. "No one is going to walk very far in a field of wheat stubble with no shoes on." A good laugh greeted this, it was easy to imagined a barefooted man being stranded like that.

Roger then continued, "A stupid story our dad told us much late, when he came home was about three German airmen who had bailed out and been rounded up by the Home Guard just outside Portsmouth, and the Navy Barracks had been ordered to take a posse out to arrest them and bring them in. Our dad explained to us that sailors were not used to this sort of job, they are supposed to fight on ships! Anyhow, three of them went off as told, taking a covered lorry with a Wren driver and armed themselves with a rifle each from the stores. It was a foul wet day, and the sailors found the airmen still standing and looking very miserable at the edge of a field in a sea of mud. The sailors indicated to the airmen to climb into the back of the lorry which they were mighty glad to do, and then the sailors prepared to climb in after them."

"You won't believe the next bit," said Roger laughing. "It was still raining, and the sailors found their blessed rifles very awkward to hold and clamber up into the lorry at the same time, so they calmly passed the rifles up to the Germans and said "Hold these a minute mate." The Germans dutifully obliged, and handed them back once the sailors were on board! It wasn't until they got back to barracks that the thought struck: perhaps they had been a trifle trusting to say the least. Their officer heard their tale and nearly had a pink fit."

Once again, Roger's listeners had a good laugh, "I can just see it happening," agreed several.

"One grisly tale we heard," continued Roger who was now thoroughly into his story telling, "was of an English pilot who bailed out from a great height, but his parachute didn't open."
"Oh God," someone said.

"He landed up on the Down," said Roger "and they say the body was three feet down, buried by the impact into the hard chalk."

"The first time when the war became real to me," continued Roger, still far away in his memories, "was when a Henkel 111 crash-landed on the Downs near the Golf Course. Us lads were quite expert at identifying different British planes, but a Heinkel 111! A real German bomber! This was something really, really different, and we couldn't wait to get on our bikes after school and go steaming up to the golf course to see. I can see it in my mind's eye now as clearly as I saw it then," continued Roger." I cycled up the chalk roadway as far as we could go, and then walked the last hundred yards to the site. The first thing I saw as I came round a stubby tree was this tail fin rising above the gorse bushes, painted a pale green-grey, with a great black German Swastika in the centre. That great German Swastika mesmerised me. I couldn't take my eyes off it, my heart pounded, 'so it is all real!' I suddenly realised. Until then all the pictures we had seen of the war and the Germans were in newspapers, but here it was actually real, yes! Right in front of my eyes."

"Go on!" said his listeners.

"Well, we walked up to plane, as close as we could get, there was quite a crowd there already, and a cordon of armed Home Guards were posted around it to keep everyone at a distance. The plane was absolutely intact except for all the bent propeller blades as it had crash-landed on its belly without the undercarriage down. As a result the cockpit was only head-high. The Home Guard however had left a small pathway open up to the cockpit and everyone was queuing up to peer in. I joined in, but I wished I hadn't. As I peered through the dim perspex, I realised that I was looking at two empty seats with blood stains all over the place. I suddenly felt sick!"

"What about the crew?" asked one of the spellbound listeners.

"We were told that there were three, one dead and one injured, but they had all been taken away."

"How old were you then?" one of the testers asked. "It was August time," calculated Roger, The day before my birthday, I was just coming up to thirteen."

"Didn't you have nightmares?"

"No, I don't think so, but the picture stuck in my mind for weeks, and I can still see it now."

"What an experience!" said a listener. "Were some of the others upset?"

"Not in our gang, because I was the tallest, and had taken first look, the others needed lifting up but I wouldn't do it, and then our gang got moved on."

The testers were still wondering what to say next, when Roger broke into a laugh "I've now got to tell you the funny end to this episode."

"I don't see anything funny about it." someone said.

"Ah, then listen to this," continued Roger. "'The next day we got a message through the grapevine that the Heinkel was not being guarded any more, and that people were up there getting souvenirs. Well, we were off again like a shot, and found people swarming all over the plane cannabalising whatever they could wrench off. Some had heavy tools with them and were pulling out seats, instruments, anything they could move. As for me, I was not squeamish, but I couldn't fancy going near that cockpit again, but I had thought about it before I came and arrived with a pair of tin snips. With these I managed to cut out of the aluminium tail fin a nice square containing part of that German Swastika. With this I was very proud and cycled home feeling pretty pleased with my trophy balanced across the handlebars. The real joke was" laughed Roger, "but we didn't know at the time, was that the plane was one of the first intact German Heinkels that the country had ever captured, and a posse of experts were on their way from London to discover all its secrets."

His audience looked astounded. "How on earth did it get unguarded?"

"It turned out to have been a monumental cock-up between the Home Guard and the army as to who had the next shift on guard."

"I can easily believe that," said a listener who was in the Home Guard himself and he laughed. "I can see them finishing their night shift on guard, no replacements in sight, and saying 'Bugger it then, I'm at work today' and going home to breakfast."

They all joined in the laughter "Well," finished Roger "as you can imagine, by the time the experts arrived, all that was left was the skeleton, anything of value had disappeared!"

"And that gentlemen," said the chief of test who had been listening, "was how we won the war," and amid more laughter the happy tea break came to a finish.

CHAPTER 7

"Come up and see me sometime"

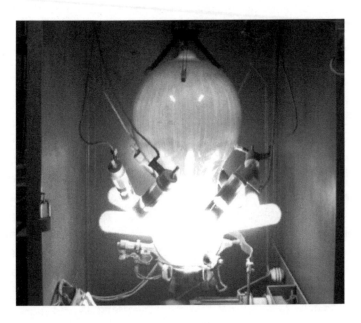

A mercury arc rectifier supplying DC current

The Rectifier Division was a little apart from the heavy machine shops, situated on the other side of the canal close to the laboratories. As such, this division and the labs were slightly divorced from older parts of the factories, and had developed a slightly different culture of their own. In particular they were the only seats of any electronics skills on the site, a rather black art to the old school, and not considered by some to be genuine engineering at all. In fact, in the view of many engineers, no one in their right mind would trust a machine or their lives to control from a few glass bottles!

Roger duly presented himself on his first day of assignment, and was immediately made to feel at home. For the first time since his arrival at the factory he was ushered to a seat and a desk, and expected to hang his coat up in a cupboard. Such refinement! Here the good old upturned greasy toolboxes were replaced by seats at a desk, and his first job was to read some literature. "This will explain what we all get up to!" he was told with a laugh.

Roger couldn't help smiling to himself. "A much better reception than the lung tester" he thought.

An engineer soon came up and introduced himself. "My name's David," he said, "and I gather I'm to be your guide whilst you are with us. It's the habit up here, although I don't expect you need any hand-holding! How's your apprenticeship going?"

"Fine," answered Roger, "I'm really enjoying myself. I've been here over a year now and the time has flown."

"That's good," said David "I also started as an 'ape' like you, but that's a few years ago now. I still treasure that time, I made some good friends then all over the factory, and they're still there now. If ever I get stuck on a problem, there's always someone who will help. What you will realise in time, is that this place is one large family most of the time. The world is an exciting place these days, all our customers want the latest, so we are always trying out new things, often getting ourselves into a real hole, and then bailing each other out!" David laughed. "If our customers knew half of what goes on sometimes, they would have a pink fit!" Roger joined in the laughter. It was infectious, although he didn't really know what he was laughing at. It was difficult to believe these engineers half the time.

"We have one main product up here that is our bread and butter," went on David "that is mercury arc rectifiers. Although the national supply is alternating current, there is still a steady demand for direct current supplies to industry, for example, large motor control systems, and electric supplies to factories for electroplating, welding and such like. On the railways they use DC motors for the London Underground and other '3rd rail' systems such as the South Coast. The main devices we build for this is a range of mercury arc rectifiers, so let's go and have a look at one."

David led the way down to their factory floor, and took him to a device consisting of a large glass dome some five foot high with six tall terminals near the base and a pool of mercury inside at the bottom. "Don't get too close," warned David, there's three thousand volts on those six terminals and it's live." Roger could indeed see the device was alive, there was a quiet hissing going on and Roger could see perpetual electric arcing going on inside the glass, the arcs starting from the six terminals inside the glass, and flashing down to a pool of mercury at the bottom. The mercury was in a perpetual state of high disturbance, the surface heaving about at the perpetual rain of arcs striking it. David explained, "These incoming terminals are at three phase, three thousand volts alternating ac supply. Inside the glass there is a vacuum, and the electric current only flows in the positive direction. The three-phase supply is first converted into six phases by a special transformer and then every terminal gives one squirt of current in turn so that the arc is rotating between the six. You can't see that because it is cycling at fifty times per second so that it looks continuous. The result is that you end up with a direct current stream coming out of that bottom terminal connected into the mercury. And "Bingo!" there you have an ac supply converted into direct current. Simple really!"

Roger nodded, he was mesmerised by the sight," I've never seen that before," he said, "it looks very impressive." "They will soon be old-fashioned," sighed David. "Modern devices just starting to appear can do the one way trick with small conducting objects that look like resistors. It will be a sad day though, we have a lot of affection for the old glass bottles."

They stood watching the rectifier for a short while, Roger being fascinated by the sight of the electric arc dancing all over the surface of the mercury in a random haphazard manner with the speed of lightning. "Of course it does!" thought Roger suddenly,"It *is* lightning, only trapped in this bottle."

David broke into his reverie "We had a lot of trouble last year," he said.

"How come?" asked Roger.

"Well, all of a sudden we started to have failures on site when quite suddenly the rectifiers would stop arcing."

WACKY DEFINITIONS

RESULTANT OF A
FORCE ON A CONDUCTOR

METAL
RECTIFIER

A SELF INDUCED
CURRENT

GENT'S

UNIT CHARGE.

Albert

"Why?" asked Roger.

"That's what we all wanted to know. We had made no changes to the product, but suddenly this crop of failures started on new installations. We traced it straight away to the failure of the vacuum, because like a valve, they only work in an almost perfect vacuum. That was the easy bit of detection, but then the trouble started. We found that hair-line cracks were developing in the compound that sealed the incoming electric terminals to the glass body, they were almost invisible but were enough to cause the vacuum to be lost."

"We were flummoxed, we had not changed our supplier of the sealing compound, and the specification had not altered. We contact the compound manufacturer, a specialist firm we had worked with for years, and they were as baffled as us." David paused, and pointed to the seals. "What you have to understand," he continued, "is that this sealing compound has a very tricky job to do, because not only does it have to retain a perfect seal for the internal vacuum, but it has to do this over a wide range of temperatures from very hot on full load in the tropics, to freezing in winter when not switched on. Now, why is that a problem?" he suddenly asked Roger.

"Is it something to do with expansion?" replied Roger cautiously.

"Dead right, you've got it in one," said David, "glass and copper have very different coefficients of expansion, so that the size of the tiny gap between the incoming electric conductor and the glass container changes with heat, and yet the seal has to maintain a perfect seal."

"How did you solve the problem then?" asked Roger.

"Well! the story became very interesting. Our supplier was also at his wits' end to sort the problem out, he is a big international concern and stood to lose a lot of business and goodwill. The root cause of the problem they explained to us was that the employee who made the compound was one of their oldest and most reliable workers, but had just retired, and the stuff was now being prepared by someone else using the same formula and the same equipment. But somehow, it wasn't turning out quite performing the same and no-one could work out why. They couldn't ask the old feller because he was very ill and they were afraid he would be taking his secret to the grave with him!"

Roger was startled, "I heard the same sort of story in big shop" he said "They've got a relatively senior man running their big milling machine, and they told me that no one else can get it right. What happened then in your case?"

David laughed. "We don't quite know, our supplier clammed up on their secrets. One serious suggestion was that the old feller used to pee into the mixture, but we never heard the end of it. Suddenly, however, the next batch was OK and we have had no more trouble since." David paused, and then suddenly said, "You know, there's still a lot of art in our business, it's not all simply pure science," and then continued. "While we're here, we might as well take a stroll round the rest of our little empire," and he led the way into the next room.

The room was small and very untidy, the centre of attention being a large table around which a few engineers were making adjustments to an absolute gaggle of bits and pieces. There were resistors, meters, electronic valves, scribbled bits of paper, oscilloscopes and items that Roger didn't recognise, all apparently wired together using a mixture of crocodile clips and bare wire ends twisted together. As they watched, the engineers stood back apparently satisfied, and then someone leaned over and pressed a switch. There was a noise nearby and an electric motor bolted to the floor suddenly started to rotate slowly. Adjustments were made on the table and the motor gradually gathered speed. When it had reached what Roger estimated as its full speed, another switch was touched on the table, and with a shrill whine the motor rapidly ground to a halt and ran up to speed in the other direction. This was repeated several times with the engineers taking copious notes and the motor obliging each time to the required commands with an ear-splitting screech of protest. No one was taking any interest of the motor, all eyes were on the meters and the recordings they were taking.

"What's going on?" asked Roger mystified.

"This is an experiment," explained David "we are trying to control the speed of that motor using electronics in its supply. If we can do this reliably there will be many applications where this will be an improvement on physical controls like rheostats for example."

"But what about that poor motor?" said Roger. "It won't last five minutes with that treatment!"

David laughed, "Don't worry about that," he said smiling "this is purely experimental. If we get really serious about some real life applications, then, firstly the motors will have to be designed to take it, and then secondly, we shall go into a real life test run."

"What's that?"

"We have special places upon the hill behind us where we can set up the whole system, electronics, motors, recording devices and the lot, and simply run it for as long as needed to check it out."

"How long is that?" asked Roger.

"It depends, but one thousand hours continuous running is common, sometimes a lot longer."

"Good Lord!" exclaimed Roger "that's a long time."

"Oh it's quite common with new equipment and ideas," said David. "Engineers are very conservative where anything new is concerned." He paused. "Actually old Hitler did us a favour over this. We use the old-time air raid shelters up on the hill for these tests. They have the advantage of being out the way, and they get subject to nasty cold and damp weather, which is often a stipulated part of the testing program." Roger laughed in surprise, and they went forward and had the experiment explained to them.

When they got back to the office, David turned to Roger and said, "I don't suppose you had air raid shelters down in Sussex, did you? I expect you had a cosy time of it down there during the war!"

Roger was indignant. "Of course we had air-raid shelters, we were in the war too you know!"

"I don't recall any stories of Sussex being *blitzed!*" said David with a wry smile.

"No," agreed Roger "not like London and yourselves of course, but by the end of the war we had collected quite a few casual bombs and casualties. It was certainly well over a hundred in our town alone!"

"Good Lord!" said David "I always pictured Sussex as a sort of country haven away from all the troubles. Why would anyone want to bomb *you?*"

Roger smiled. "Well, we had airfields around us, and we were in the thick of it during the Battle of Britain. We had plenty of air raid warnings when there were dog-fights going on overhead."

"And did you all go down in the shelters?"

"Not a chance!" laughed Roger. "Some of the grownups did, but we were kids at the time, and we used to enjoy watching. We got pretty expert at identifying planes, although most dogfights were way up too high. We could hear the machine gun bursts, and we would climb up on the roof of the packing shed to try a get a better view. That was down on the nursery where we often played all day in the summertime," Roger explained.

"But didn't your parents call you down?" asked David in surprise.

"I think they did just once" said Roger, "when there was a sudden rattling on the glass of the green-houses as a load of spent cartridges came down from above, but we were coming down by then any-rate to hunt for souvenirs."

David was intrigued- "Tell me more" he said as they sat down comfortably in the office.

Roger starting laughing. "I remember a good laugh we had one day. There was a foreman on the nursery called Ernie who was really scared about everything, and when the sirens went, he used to stop what he was doing and hurry down into the stoke-hole where the heating boiler was situated between No.1 and No.2 greenhouses, and he would stay crouched there underneath the big corrugated tin roof until the 'all-clear' sounded. Everyone knew he used to do this, although most of the staff just got on with their work."

"He wouldn't have lasted long up here!" said David.

"Well, one day," continued Roger "when he was down the stoke-hole during an air raid alarm, my brother and our cousin crept silently up to the stoke-hole carrying a large lump of stone. They heaved it up into the air and it came down with a thunderous crash on the tin roof!" Roger started laughing again at the memory, and David joined in.

"What happened then?" grinned David.

"Poor old Ernie," said Roger, "he came flying out of the stoke-hole, ran a hundred yards down the path as though the devil was behind him, and flew across the road on to the village green where there was a big communal shelter. The 'all-clear' went soon after, but they couldn't get him to come out for about two hours."

"You were a rum set of beggars" said David ruefully. "I feel quite sorry the chap."

"There's a horrible twist to the story," said Roger. "A few years later, towards the end of the war, the Germans started dropping large bombs on parachutes. They were known as 'landmines' and did a wide area of damage. One day, when Ernie was on his compulsory stint as an air raid warden, one of these landmines dropped into the enclosed back garden of a pub where three or four people were drinking. We were told afterwards that the carnage was terrible, but poor old Ernie, of all people, got the horrible job of going round with four sacks, and trying to the put the matching bits of bodies into respective sacks. Apparently, he did it, but refused ever after to speak about it."

Roger continued. "Actually," he said with a grimace, "we had a landmine dropped one night only about a quarter of a mile from our house. I can still picture it," he said reflectively. "I was half asleep at the time, and there was suddenly this tremendous bang with no warning. It sounded mighty close, and I distinctly heard a great rush of wind go past the house rattling our roof on the way and the breaking of glass somewhere, followed almost straight away by a rush of wind in the other direction, and then there was total silence. It was a very eerie sensation. I felt for a minute that I was having a dream, and was just laying there imagining it."

"That's called a willing suspension of belief," said David. "What happened next?"

"Well, I could hear noises starting all over the place, and everyone in our house was waking up and starting to shout, so I got up as well and we all went downstairs as we didn't know what else to do. None of us was hurt, but the curious thing was that we found the front door had been blown half off its hinges, and yet we hadn't lost a single pane of glass from any of the downstairs windows. Then dad came down looking very shaken, he had already woken up and was looking out the front bedroom window at the time. He saw the land-mine on its parachute drifting past. He was still thinking he was dreaming when it went off and several panes of glass were blown out of the bedroom windows on each side of him, but his pane stayed intact!"

"I can believe it" said David "blasts can do the most peculiar things!"

The next morning in the office, David said to him with a chuckle, "See that desk over there?"

"Yes" said Roger, "what about it?"

"Does it look OK to you?" and he grinned.

"Why yes," said Roger puzzled, looking at it more closely. It looked very ordinary, there were papers in a neat pile, and an IN basket half full, a chair pulled up tidily underneath, and indeed nothing exceptional at all.

"You wait and see next Monday," said David. "The lads have done a great job there."

"What do you mean?" asked Roger. "That desk is Curly's desk, and he is on holiday." David was obviously enjoying himself. "They've turned his desk round, and bolted it to the partition behind, with the handles moved over to this back side and screwed into position. He'll have the shock of his life when he tries to open the drawers!" and he laughed.

Roger soon found himself helping engineers set up tests and he found the experiences he had had so far were now proving very useful. He was often getting left to set up and run tests himself, and the time passed quickly. He also became aware of some very dominant characters in the division that he realised were very similar to Skipper in Switchgear Division. In fact they were often involved in tests and meetings with the other side of the canal, and he became very aware of the good fellowship, mutual respect and also the fun they all shared together. One dominant character in this new division was Sammy Dale, who, Roger found, seem to an expert in nearly everything. Apart from being a highly respected electrical engineer, he was an expert in fishing, photography, pronunciation of Welsh names, cars, motorbikes, and in both making violins and playing them.

One evening Roger was over in the Magnet Club gingerly playing a Chopin prelude on the piano when Sam appeared and was obviously not satisfied with Roger's playing. He immediately took over and replayed the prelude, explaining to Roger by example where to accentuate some of the hidden melodic line! The more Roger got to know Sam, the more he became convinced that Sam could just about do anything he put his hand to! Indeed, a few days later at lunch, Sam announced that he was buying a new car. It was a new model from Austin, and he announced it would have the highest power to weight ratio of any car on the general market. This was of great interest to all at the dinner table, as everyone had a high respect for Sam's knowledge of cars, he was always discussing them and changing his own every six months or so. Everyone was very keen to see just what monster Sam would produce next. To everyones' surprise, he rolled up three days later in a brand new Austin Mini-Cooper S, the last thing anyone expected! He then proceeded to go into great details on the performance, and demonstrated with great effect on the waste ground behind the building later that afternoon.

Another person who had a quiet but subtle influence on the whole division was the divisional manager himself, a Mr Gallizia. He was an Italian engineer who had been in England for many years. He was greatly liked and respected by everyone who knew him and had become the perfect English gentleman. He would carefully listen to any problem and invariably offer some useful contributions in a very unassuming manner. One personal feature of his was his practice of regularly turning up at all social functions with two "nieces" — very pretty, charming, happy ladies, and a lot younger than himself. This often raised eyebrows, but being the man he was, nobody ever said anything. He was great fun on these occasions although he kept strict discipline at work.

One typical story told to Roger had occurred a few weeks earlier, when Mr Gallizia was on the shop floor assisting some engineers in examining a failed rectifier unit. It was his frequent practice to do this, as he greatly enjoyed getting into overalls and joining in technical problems with his staff. On this occasion when he was in the middle of the discussion, a carrier came in with a parcel labelled "For the personal attention of Mr Gallizia." The carrier, rather a rough diamond and apparently not in the best of moods, lurched up to Mr Gallizia and said "I've got a parcel here for some bugger called Gerlisher or some bloody name. Where can I find 'im?" There was a moments silence all round and then Mr Gallizia apparently very politely pointed out to him the long way up to his office, and as the man lumbered off, he himself took the short way up and was sitting at his desk when the man strolled in!

David was telling the story. "No-one knows what was said in that office, but the carrier left after a few minutes with a face looking distinctly sick. After that the boss came back to the shop floor, and never said a word about it!" Roger enjoyed that story, he had met Mr Gallizia several times, and could just imagine the whole scene, it was so typical.

A few weeks later, Roger himself witnessed an incident concerning the boss that filled him with astonishment. He was in a group on the shop floor, where the boss was in the middle of a technical discussion with some engineers on yet another problem. A foreman, obviously in a worried state, came up from the shop floor next door and tried to quietly interrupt. The boss spotted him, stopped what he was saying, and turned to this foreman with the slightest of frowns, and asked him what the trouble was. "I'm so sorry to interrupt sir," he stammered, but I've just had a telephone call to say that my house is on fire. Will it be alright if I go home?"

There was apparently no question of his rushing off without permission, politeness was everything in MAR! "Of course!" said the boss without hesitating, and, amid offers of help all round, the man sped off. Everyone was too startled to think much about it at the time, but later on Roger heard the tale being repeated all around the factory, and realised that the story would go down as another remarkable anecdote to be treasured.

A few days later, Roger's mentor David was called across to Switchgear Division to help them out with a control problem. They were developing a new voltage controller for large power station generators. "For their new 500MW generators," he explained to Roger, "and something isn't quite right. Apparently they can't stop the generator output voltage slowly going up and down, and the government inspectors are due next week. Our chief engineer is having forty fits about it, as this is a brand new venture for us, and he says we daren't make a mess of it."

"Why are you involved, can't Switchear Division sort it out themselves?" asked Roger.

"When something goes wrong in this place," explained David, "it's all hands to the pump, there's no demarcation between divisions. What happen is that anybody from anywhere who can possibly help is called in by management and told to get down to it, and sort it out. The good thing is then that they leave you in peace to get on with it. They don't panic and keep leaning over your shoulder like I have seen in some places."

"Do you know anything about voltage regulators?" asked Roger.

"Not a lot!" said David cheerfully, "and certainly not for these monster machines attached to the British National Grid system," he laughed. "In fact, nobody does in this place, that's why the chief engineer is in such a flap. He himself had insisted we must include the voltage controllers in the initial contract because he felt it was too infra-dig to keep on supplying some of the largest generators in the world, and yet have to go outside to subcontract the voltage controllers. Apparently, these controllers are the vital component, because their failure can mess up the local British National Grid system."

"Well, I wish you luck," said Roger as David departed cheerfully, taking a few extra meters with him in case.

David came back the same afternoon and called Roger over. "Roger!" he said, "I'm enlisting you to help with the problem we've got with these wretched voltage controllers. We need someone to get down to some basic studies."

"But I don't know anything about them!" said Roger looking startled.

"Join the club" said David cheerfully. "That's nothing new in this place. I've been over in Main Test where we are trying to get them to work, but we are realising that none of us really understand the first thing about the stability problems of generators coupled to the National Grid. It would seem it is rather more complicated business than we realised."

Roger swallowed, "but how can I help?" he asked.

"What we've got to do," explained David, "is to get a grip on first principles, and that means a bit of study. Now all the best technical literature is in the American IEEE papers, and we have done a quick search, and picked out a few that might help us. I want you to go and get them out of our library, we keep all the top technical journals there, and plough through them to see if they will give us any clues what to do."

Roger went off with a list of references, and came staggering back with three hefty volumes of technical papers. Mercifully, most of the individual papers were quite short, about six to eight pages, and beautifully printed with all the mathematical equations very easy to read. "We've got to give it to the Yanks," said David looking at them "the quality of their technical output during the war and since has been absolutely second to none. They contain the latest research on all these subjects, and they are very well explained. It's no wonder that all round the world engineers are learning English, it's much safer than translations into their own language."

Roger got stuck into the papers, and soon realised that the voltage control of large generators was a vital component of the whole power station! If voltage control was lost, the generator could either run up to a very high voltage, upset the whole output of the station, and maybe cause severe insulation damage to the generator, or even — much worse — if the controller tried to drop the voltage, the set could lose synchronism with the supply. This would cause an immediate heavy over-current and trip the set off the system. If the set was at that time pouring out its full power into the system, the driving steam turbine would start to raise the speed in a dramatic fashion, and unless the governor control acted correctly within a matter of seconds, the speed would get so high that the whole set would literally blow up, including the turbine, the generator and maybe anyone nearby! There were recorded cases of this having happened. Roger stared at the papers, and realised he now had a real job on his hands.

After three days pouring through several papers, Roger settled on one which seemed to be exactly what was wanted, and he sat down to understand it thoroughly. He remembered an incident earlier with the Works' resident consulting engineer named Doctor Friedlander, "The Doc" to everyone. He was a small very quiet engineer with a reputation for having been trained with one of the top European engineering firms before the war. He had fled to England to escape the rise of Hitler and the Nazi regime. He was now very much in demand in the works on a whole range of queries, and on that earlier occasion had asked Roger to study a complicated paper of the Doc's in connection with a magnetic field problem. After two days, Roger had gone back to him exasperated, and confessed that he couldn't understand a word of the paper.

The Doc simply smiled at him kindly, took the blame for a possible poor translation of his work into English and said, "I know just how you feel, but I want you to go back and start again at the very first sentence. When you come to the very first sentence that you don't fully understand, come back and see me."

Roger had gone back angrily to the paper, and started again. He felt himself saying, "Well, of course I

"Best apprentice we've ever had!"

see that!" and he found himself pressing on and on and at a loss to pick out one particular sentence to go back with. Suddenly, Roger realised he had got to the end and he had understood it all! Roger now applied himself in the same way, and soon gained confidence that he knew what the paper was saying.

The next day, David came in with a broad grin on his face. "How are you getting on?" he asked.

"Not too bad" said Roger "I think I am beginning to understand how it all works." "That's great!" said David, "because I've got good news for you. We cracked it last night, the regulator is now running perfectly."

"How do you mean?" asked Roger.

"We had a blitz on it last night, and we had Donald with us from the Lab. He has done some work on stability problems before, and after a couple of hours up to 2 a.m. trying new arrangements of some damper windings, he got it to work perfectly. The chief engineer came in this morning and was mighty relieved, because the official inspectors are due on Friday!"

Roger did not know whether to laugh or cry. He had now spent over a week stewing over the technical papers, "Does that mean my time has been wasted?" he asked.

"Oh no, not a bit of it!" replied David, "making it work by only fiddling around with it is just a start. It's very important we get to the bottom of the theory. Otherwise, the whole device remains a bag of mystery, and we won't be allowed to make any more."

Roger felt relieved and pressed on with his study until he had a clear picture in his head. David then assembled all the engineers involved in the work and they gathered around Roger for a briefing. Roger now realised he was in the hot seat, so he started hesitantly. "The vital thing we have to do is to write down the regulator exactly in terms of the loop gains, the feedbacks and the time delays in each component. Do we know all these?"

"Yes," said a designer, "here they are, and we are fairly confident they are correct."

"Right," said Roger, "but the nasty bit now is to link these in with the mathematical model of the generator itself and produce a comprehensive joint set of equations. I have worked out the set we need from these technical papers, and the complete set of equations looks like this," and Roger produced a formidable set of equations, all inter-related. "The job now is to fill in all the parameters, and then solve the equations to give us a set of answers telling us under what conditions we are stable, and when we are not."

The group looked at the paper, and someone said plaintively, "But these equations are very complex, there will be weeks of work needed to solve them all!"

"You mean months!" said another, "and even then we shall probably get some wrong!"

There was a pause, and then David spoke up. "There may be a way round this, I have read of an electronic calculating machine being developed at the NPL, that's the National Physics Laboratory in Teddington. They claim this new machine can solve a set of ten simultaneous equations in under ten minutes."

"Right" said senior design engineer turning to Roger, "we'll help you to complete all the numbers in the sets of equations, and off you go to Teddington!"

Roger did as he was bid, and inside a week they had assembled between them a pile of pages with the formidable sets of equations tabulated with numbers against them. David had contacted the NPL who said they would be delighted to help, and Roger set off with the precious set of papers. When he arrived the staff at NPL were as good as their word, and Roger returned feeling very pleased with the interest they had shown. Their new machine had worked perfectly even to their own amazement, and Roger returned to Witton with the results he wanted. Back in the office the results were then plotted and recorded in a detailed report, and the problem was considered understood and resolved. Roger was very pleased to have been part of the team, especially when they received a formal letter of thanks from the head of Turbo-generator Design with a copy to the chief engineer.

There was an interesting follow up to the episode that caused considerable merriment. About five months later, Roger received a telephone call from the NPL where an extremely courteous voice, full of apologies for troubling him, said that they were getting embarrassed because Witton had not paid the bill they had submitted for the solution of the simultaneous equations. It amounted to the princely sum of £12.15s.6d. Roger made enquiries, and finally tracked down the invoice to where it was, still sitting in limbo in No.1 Receiving stores in Switchgear Works. When asked, the storekeeper rummaged around in a large pile, and finally found the well-thumbed invoice and explained his problem to Roger. "This invoice makes no sense, in the first place it is addressed, 'For the attention of Mr. Roger—?' and apart from not knowing who the hell to contact, we have not even received any bottle!'

"What bottle?" asked Roger totally flummoxed.

"Well, it says here on the invoice," 'For the supply of solutions for 6 sets of differential equations', and coming from the National Physics Laboratory, we've been searching for the bottle."

Roger went back and related the story to David who roared with laughter. "Logically he was dead right," he said. "You normally find 'solutions' from the medics in a bottle!"

"I know," said Roger. "Funnily enough, we had exactly the same sort of mis-understanding once down on the nursery. My brother and I, even after we had gone to college, used to enjoy going back on the nursery at holiday times, and joining in again with our old workmates. One Christmas, we joined them in the packing shed at lunchtime, and one of the old faithful retainers, old Percy, in his broad Sussex accent, said to my brother, 'Waal John, waat yu be doin' now up theer in Lunnon?' and John, feeling a little self-conscious of his new elevated lifestyle, said 'I'm up at London University, taking a special degree course in advanced physics.'" Roger started to laugh at the memory, "They all sat there nodding their heads wisely and staring at the floor. No one understood what on earth John was talking about. Then at last Percy spoke. 'Arr good! Waal, you'd better give your old Dad a good dose, 'e aint been looking too well lately,' and they all nodded in agreement.

David laughed "It's this wonderful language of ours, I'm sorry for foreigners" he said, and pressed Roger to join him over at the Magnet Club for a beer.

CHAPTER 8

"Mind my bike"

Dr. Wilson's unique trousers dryer

Roger's next assignment was to the laboratories next door to MAR, and he approached this post with considerable interest. He had heard a great deal beforehand about the manager, a certain Doctor Wilson who was a rather idiosyncratic character with many quite astonishing tales to his credit. "Like so many in these works," mused Roger to himself as he arrived the next Monday morning.

Roger had already met Doctor Wilson at a social function some months earlier, it had been an annual event to which all graduate apprentices were expected to attend. The event was a slide presentation by the Doctor of his latest summer holiday travels, and the occasion had become a regular, almost constitutional event in the works. Roger had attended not knowing what to expect, and had thoroughly enjoyed the whole evening. The Doctor proved to be a most entertaining speaker, and his talk had covered an extensive tour he had made around Europe just before the war. He showed a wide range of slides of various architectures, pointing out any civil engineering problems involved, and illustrating where new building innovations had developed. He had also covered world-famous sculptures and paintings, always with some added snippets of interesting background history, plus pictures and comments on railway and road developments. Interlaced with all these were pictures of electrical installations, particularly of some unusual continental country voltage distribution systems in rather odd places. He managed to find some household connect systems which were extremely crude, in some cases just bare 11 kv wires strung up between houses with string, and highly dangerous- if not lethal. He obviously enjoyed finding these, and they added a useful touch of electrical appreciation merriment to the evening.

Among his own staff he had rather a mixed reputation, as he cultivated the appearance of a mad scientist but caused irritation by often presenting other peoples' technical papers as his own. He would normally take the genuine author with him to deal with answering questions afterwards while he busied himself packing up the slides!

One classic tale about the Doctor concerned a train trip he made to London during the war. He had been called down to the London head office for an important meeting, and had cycled some eight miles from his home outside Birmingham to Snow Hill station to catch the early morning London train. He had cycled, as petrol was non-existent for private motoring during the war. The train was the well patronised business train, non-stop, and headed by the best GWR Castle class steam engines. Unfortunately for the Doctor, this particular day it came on to pour with rain during his cycle journey, and he found himself getting on the train with his trousers absolutely soaking wet from the knees downwards. He felt he couldn't attend the meeting in such a state, so he went and locked himself in the toilet. He was travelling first class as usual, and proceeded to hang his trousers out of the little toilet window to dry. Obviously, technical inspiration had got the better of common sense, and inside two minutes the trousers had been snatched away by something near the line, and they were never seen again. "What a predicament!" said Roger to the laughing group who were telling him the story. "What on earth did he do?"

"Very simple for him!" they continued. "He simply pulled the communication chord, the train ground to a mighty halt, and when the guard found him, he calmly shouted through the toilet door his predicament and what he wanted done." The upshot was that the train got under way again, with the Doctor staying resident in the first-class toilet, and when they reached Paddington, a harassed tailor was waiting with two new pairs of trousers over his arm; they had been hastily made to verbal measurements wired through by the railway company. Apparently, one pair was very satisfactory, and the Doctor continued on his way."

"Well I'm jiggered!" exclaimed Roger, "I would never have had the nerve to do that! But" he mused to himself later, "I hope I will never become crackers enough to think of hanging my trousers out of a train window in the first place!"

In the laboratory he found a hive of activity as the place was being prepared for a visitors' open day, and Roger's first job was to help make the place look as clean and tidy as possible, and help out in preparing desk notices about the items and experiments on display. On the first table he was introduced to an electronic brain-child built by one of the staff to prove that the odds were exactly fifty-fifty every time you spun a coin whatever the previous sequence of calls. "I know about this," said Roger. "It's a funny business. I came face to face with it once at a roulette table. I had joined in, and was placing very small bets on whether the red or black colour would come up on the next spin. I knew of course that the chances would still be fifty-fifty every throw, but if there had been three red calls in a row, it was quite impossible not to bet that the next call would be black!"

"That's just what this device proves," grinned the staff member. "No matter how many of one sequence, the next throw is still fifty-fifty."

"How can this do that?" asked Roger peering at the table. There was a mass of untidy wiring, connecting some resistors and valves together, a push button at the front, and two prominent lamp bulbs, one on each side, labelled "heads" and "tails" respectively. There were also two numerical counter display units side by side at the back. "What does it all do?" asked Roger without the faintest idea in his head.

"It's to do with mathematics, and I'll tell you another time," said the staff member. (See appendix 3) "The job now is to make this desk look a bit tidier. If we can," he added, shaking his head.

There were several other exhibits that intrigued Roger, the first being a stroboscope example where a large disc mounted on the end of a motor could be rotated over a range of speeds by, once again, an electronic speed control system. "The Doctor just loves plugging electronics," thought Roger to himself. A stroboscopic light had been arranged to shine on to the disc, and so arranged that at a certain speed the disc would appear stationary.

"Like the wagon wheels in an old movie" explained the staff member who had set it up. He demonstrated to Roger.

There was a black ink drawing on the disc of a man's face, which bore an excellent resemblance to the Doctor himself, and when the engineer adjusted the motor speed until it synchronised with the strobe light, the face appeared, it was a very clear picture and Roger found himself laughing out loud. The speed control system was very smooth, and by slightly speeding up the motor, the demonstrator then made the face slowly creep clockwise, or by reducing the speed, creep anti-clockwise. He then held the speed constant with the picture exactly upside down, much to the amusement of several staff who had gathered to watch.

"I like the picture," said Roger "who drew it?"

"An apprentice in the drawing office named Loft," explained the engineer. "We have admired his cartoons in the Apprentices Journal, so we gave him a photo to copy, and he came up with this!"

"It's very good," said Roger "I'm most impressed."

Another interesting exhibit was a series of adjustable weights on a long shaft which was being used to exhibit critical speed problems.

The shaft could be rotated at certain speeds without any vibrations at all, but at certain speeds a distinct wobble could be heard and seen both physically and on an oscilloscope. The oscilloscope enabled even the smallest vibrations to be displayed quite clearly on an electronic screen, including multiple harmonics of any vibrations developing. By slight adjustments to the weights, vibrations could be made to increase or disappear, and the speeds at which they occurred could be changed by adjusting the rotor length or the position of the supporting bearings. The mechanical engineer in charge of the exhibit explained to Roger, "Critical speed understanding is a very important design consideration for the large generators, and as customers keep expecting bigger and bigger units for efficiency saving, so the critical speed issue becomes more and more important. Large rotors weighing thirty to forty tons, rotating at fifty revs per second, are now running normally at a speed in between their second and third critical speeds, quite a hair-raising situation unless you know exactly what you are doing!"

Roger watched the rotor spinning away, and said to the engineer, "I'm afraid I'm an electrical engineer basically, and although we covered critical speeds at college, I am still a bit hazy on the basic physics."

"You are not the only one" laughed the engineer. "Car drivers go and have their wheels balanced when they have a new tyre, and take it as a simple garage job, but the physics is really quite complex, balancing machines tell the garage where to add the balancing weights, but I don't expect many know any more than that!" "I'm afraid that includes me," smiled Roger.

The engineer took out from the drawer a piece of string with a weight on the end. "I use this simple example to get the principle across," he said. "Take hold of the end of this piece of string and let the weight hang down as a pendulum." Roger held it and the weight hung down about four feet. "Right, now first get it steady and then gently start moving your hand back and forth sideways by about an inch quite quickly, a sort of horizontal shaking at a speed of about three or four times a second." Roger did as he was bid and although the top of the string was moving with his hand, the weight at the bottom hardly moved at all. "Right, that's because your speed of shake is well above that pendulum's critical frequency. Now gently slow down your speed of shake, and see what happens?" Roger slowed right down, and when he reached about one shake every two seconds, the weight at the bottom started to swing with his hand, and quite violently.

"Wow, steady on!" laughed the engineer, "You're not playing conkers! You'll crack your knuckles in a minute. Just move your hand very slightly to and fro, you can feel the natural rhythm." Roger found this to be so, he only had to do the slightest flicks on the string each way in time with the natural swing to keep the weight sailing backwards and forwards in a wide arc. "You've got it!" smiled the engineer. "You are now flicking the string at the critical speed of the pendulum, so with the bare minimum of input you can build up a wide oscillation of the whole device. That's what happens at the critical speed of any rotating device and we can demonstrate it on this model. On a large generator rotor, of course, such swinging would lead to a mechanical catastrophe."

"It's like a grandfather clock," said Roger, "we've got one at home and I've noticed that the mechanism only gives the pendulum a very small nudge every so often."

"That's right," agreed his tutor "we had better get on now, but if you are really interested, come back when this charade of an exhibition is over, and I'll go into it more fully. There's a lot more to it than this simple demo."

The visitors' day took place that weekend, and the deputy met him in the Monday morning with a broad grin on his face "Well, how do you think the day went?" he asked.

Roger had been in attendance on the Saturday, and had enjoyed explaining the "heads or tails" device to many visitors. He was not sure how many actually believed his explanations, despite the clear proof from the growing number of tries that were made, but on the whole he felt pleased. "We had a good number of visitors," said Roger, "and I thought on the whole the day was very successful."

"Ah, but you went home before the silly bit," chuckled the deputy. "I'm afraid you won't see Doctor Wilson for a few days"

"Why so?" enquired Roger.

"Well, we were busy closing down after everyone had gone, when the Doctor noticed some apprentices larking about round the back on their bicycles." "What were they doing?" asked Roger with interest, "I'm a keen cyclist myself."

"These lads were running along pushing their bikes from behind by holding the saddle, and when up to speed they were leaning over, grabbing the handlebars and leap-frogging over on to the saddle as they were moving!"

"Not bad," said Roger, "I've never tried that."

"I don't recommend it" laughed the deputy, "but dear old Doctor Wilson, who was in a very good mood at the end of his very successful day, saw this and thought he would have a try himself!"

"Never!" exclaimed Roger in alarm.

"You don't know him like we do!" laughed the deputy, "He is always interested in something new, especially anything in the nature of a challenge, so he gets his bike out, has a go, and of course crashes to a heap on the ground. He wasn't badly hurt, but quite winded and we had to take him home in a car. We have had a call this morning to say that he has a bad back, and won't be in for a few days."

Roger went and found the mechanical engineer who had shown him the critical speed model. "Can you spare a minute?" asked Roger, "there are still some things that puzzle me"

"Fire away" said the engineer cheerfully, "but let's get a coffee first and sit down in my office."

After they were sitting comfortably Roger said "Well, the first thing is, although I can understand the pendulum you showed me, how can this apply to a solid steel rotor, and also, how does it get a small vibration to start with?"

"Two questions at once!" smiled the engineer, "let's take one at a time. First of all, although I started on the pendulum, exactly the same principle applies to a violin string. It has a natural frequency dependent upon the length and the tension, and in fact it has a whole range of natural frequencies called its harmonics, you should have covered these in physics."

"Yes, I know that" said Roger, " but a rotor does not twang like a violin string!"

"That's where you're quite wrong," interrupted the engineer. "All materials are elastic up to a point, especially metals, and you have to calculate a rotor as a rod of metal between two bearings, and it can 'twang'", as you call it, just like a piece of elastic. The only difference is the movement is measured in thousandths of an inch only, not visible to the naked eye, but it is still there and you can feel it with your hand on the bearing, and it soon gets noisy. The actual measurement itself is quite measurable with instruments. OK so far?"

"Carry on," said Roger sipping his coffee.

"Well the disturbance to start the vibration is because no rotor is exactly perfect in that it is impossible to be sure that the centre of gravity is exactly on the centre line of rotation. In fact, because a completed rotor is made of many parts, if you take a cross section at different positions, you would find that the centre of gravity wanders a little as you go down the shaft. Only very slightly mind you, but at three thousand revs per minute, everything becomes important."

"I can see that," said Roger. He had been involved in Big Shop with helping fix large copper windings into the slots on large rotors. "Carry on."

"Well, this very small out-of-centre means that when it is spinning, this is reflected in a push one side and then the other on the bearings holding the rotor in position, which is exactly the same as your little nudge on the string. When the frequency of this little nudge hits a critical frequency of the rotor itself, then your 'twanging' as you so elegantly put it, can take off!"

"Thank you," said Roger "that's great"! I think I see now what you mean."

"I'll show you something else," said the engineer, warming to his subject, and he produced another piece of string from his drawer with two weights on it, one at the end as before, and one in the centre. "Here, take this and shake it as you did before to get the bottom weight swinging" Roger did this and at the same frequency as before, the bottom weight swung to and fro with the slightest nudging of his hand, with the string staying straight and the centre weight merely swinging with the string in its central position. "Good! that's the first critical as before, now double your speed of nudging and try and get the middle weight to swing as though it was on its own." Roger speeded up, and quite suddenly the middle weight .started to swing wildly as though it simply was indeed on its own, and to his surprise, the bottom weight came to almost rest in the central position. As the middle weight swung out, the string went out at an angle almost

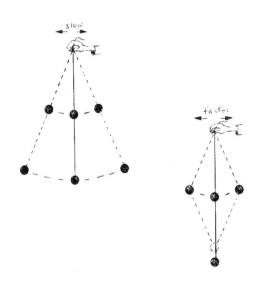

as if something was holding the bottom of the string in a fixed vertical plane. "Excellent, excellent," beamed the engineer "You've caught it exactly! That is now the second critical, and the same principle applies to our rotors." Roger went on swinging, he was quite taken with this toy, and went back to the slower swing when the first weight took off and the second stopped its own swings. "This is amazing!" he said, I could play with this for ages!"

"Right!" said his tutor, this is where it gets more complicated. A rotor has a number of critical frequencies or speeds like that piece of string, we have to design the beast so that the working running speed is not near any of these critical."

"Can you actually design for critical speeds?" asked Roger in surprise. "Oh yes, of course. The basic mathematics are just as well known for rotors as they are for a simple violin string, but it is not quite an exact science, and that's why there is a lot of testing of a new machine before it can leave the factory. The key problem for modern large generators, is that the rotors have become so long that the running speed is greater than the first designed critical, in other words we have an enormous mass of steel whizzing round where the fundamental, or first critical is above what you called the first 'twanging' frequency. In fact modern designs are planning to run even above the second critical."

"How do you make them safe then?" interrupted Roger.

"Well, first of all, once we have found the critical speeds for a specific rotor, they are fixed and never change, so we know where we are. The tricky piece then is to make sure that the 'twanging', you know..." he suddenly interrupted himself "I do like that word 'twanging', I'm going to use that myself in future'"

Roger nodded his head in appreciation. "Well, as I was saying, we have to make sure that when we reach a 'twanging' speed, the vibration is not bad enough to cause a serious vibration that could get out of control," he paused. "Are you with me so far?"

"Carry on" said Roger.

The engineer nodded and continued. "If we approach a critical, and the vibration is starting to sound nasty, we have to slow down and stop, and apply some balancing just like the garage man does with a new tyre, because, of course, we have to make sure we can get past this critical point and carry on increasing speed until we reach the running design speed."

"Who decides when a vibration is sounding 'nasty'" asked Roger.

"Myself," said the engineer, "it's part of my job, and I'm joined by the Chief Designer, and of course Ernie Jukes from Outside Erection, we all gather together for these tests."

"Ernie Jukes?" asked Roger, he had not heard the name before.

"You'll get to know him in time," laughed the engineer. "He makes all the final decisions because he has to get the machine running at the power station with the world and his wife watching. He has been in the business all his life and has a vast amount of experience. He has a nose for these things, and I have seen him placing a hand on a bearing when the noise is sounding rough and calmly shouting, 'go a bit faster, it's OK', and he is always right. Engineers like him are the salt of the earth."

"There was a bad accident a few years ago at another factory," said the engineer "you may have heard of it when you were in Main Test?"

"Yes" said Roger "about the over-speed that failed?"

"Not quite right, it wasn't on over-speed, it was when they were checking out the first critical speed."

"It was a competitor wasn't it?" asked Roger.

"It's all the same among us experts," said his tutor "one man's troubles gets shared with us all."

"What exactly happened then?" asked Roger.

"The testers were approaching the expected first critical speed, when the noise started getting quite nasty."

"I know the normal noise, that's bad enough," said Roger. He remembered vividly his walk past a full speed rotor in the over-speed pit when he was in Test, he had been very scared at the time, and his ears had not stopped ringing for over an hour.

"Good! then you can imagine the scene. Well there were important business pressures at the time to get the rotor through its tests as quickly as possible, and the testers decided to carry on increasing speed. Apparently, although the noise was quite bad, they increased speed gently, and much to their relief, the vibrations died away and they reached running speed with no more trouble. Then the problem arose when they decided to finish the run, because as they slowed down and approached the critical speed point where they had experienced trouble on the way up, the vibrations and noise was worse than before and they became too scared to slow down any further, so they speeded up again to where there was no vibration, and retired to have a think!"

"Good Heavens!" exclaimed Roger, "what did they do?"

After a lot of debate over the next two days, they decided that the only thing was do a high speed shut down and pray that they got through the critical speed point without too much damage."

"Did it work?"

"Unfortunately No!, they cleared the area of staff as a precaution, tried to shut down as quickly as they could, but as they

"Are you the same man who cut my hair last time?"
"No son, I've only been here 6 months."

went through this critical point, the rotor simply exploded like a bomb". The engineer smiled. "There's more in this business than simple science you know!"

"I'm getting well aware of that," said Roger "I wouldn't like to have to make decisions like that!"

"The engineer shrugged, "You never know, somebody has to!"

Roger's next task was to try and help a staff member wire up a complicated arrangement of small transformers linked together by devices called silicon rectifiers. The experiment was to check out a recent American paper on how to make magnetic amplifiers with instantaneous response. The deputy handed out the quite small silicon rectifiers saying "Be careful with these, they are the only ones we've got, they quite expensive, and there are very fragile."

"How do you mean, fragile?" asked the staff man.

"They are very susceptible to over-current or over-voltage. Make sure you read their ratings and keep well within those figures!"

"No problem," said his companion cheerfully, and he and Roger set to work to sort out the diagrams in the paper and wire everything together, including attaching recording meters. When they had finished his companion carried out a final check and said, "Everything looks about right, let's switch on and see how it goes!"

Roger switched on, there was a slight "poof" noise, and all the meters went back to zero. "Bloody hell!" said the tester. "What have we done?" and he sniffed one of the rectifiers. There was a faint smell of burning. "I think," he said ponderously "we've buggered it up!" He paused, "Ah well, that's the way experiments go," he said dismissively. "Before we try and sort out what's wrong, how about a cup of tea?" Roger felt he had to agree, and off they went.

Once they were seated with their mugs the tester laughed "The deputy won't be pleased about his precious rectifiers, I imagine about half of them have gone west from the smell! So we shall have to hang about a few days until we get some more."

"But what went wrong?" asked Roger.

"I've no idea yet," said the tester, "but with new experiments we get quite used to hiccups like this, it's probably something quite trivial, most likely we've got some of those silly rectifiers the wrong way round." He suddenly changed the subject. "By the way, where do you come from if you don't mind me asking? you certainly don't have a Midlands' accent."

"No," laughed Roger feeling at ease, "I'm a Sussex man, and until I came here I had only been North of London once before in my life."

"You haven't missed much!" the tester continued, "I come from Yorkshire and I don't take to this area at all, but I enjoy the job so I suppose that's the main thing."

"I came up here at the beginning of the war," explained Roger. "I was only twelve years old, not long at the grammar school, and the whole school was suddenly evacuated up here to a place called Southwell in Nottinghamshire. I remember the first night very well, we were all given sleeping bags in a big school hall, and a very cheerful man was in charge. By then we had got over leaving our mums at home on Worthing station, and were quite looking forward to the adventure. Someone asked him, "Do you get any air raids and bombs up here?" and when he answered 'Good Lord No!' we were all very disappointed because that was the last thing we wanted to hear"

The tester laughed "You set of bloodthirsty little beggars!"

Roger joined in laughing, "Well we were quite young you know."

"You were certainly disappointed then in Southwell" said the tester, "I don't suppose Jerry ever heard of the place."

"Maybe" grinned Roger, "but we didn't wait long enough to find out. The threat of an invasion had disappeared, thanks to our winning the 'Battle of Britain', and all the parents back home got fed up and all the boys started to drift home. We were all very pleased, because our school formally re-opened in Worthing after Easter in nineteen-forty-two , and we were all back home for the Summer holidays. My younger brother John was also evacuated" said Roger, "but his junior school went the day after us and ended up in the mining area of Mansfield Woodhouse. I myself had ended up billeted in a fairly well-to-do house with the bank manager, but poor old John found himself in a miner's cottage with a loo in the back yard! He told me later that very soon after he arrived, and sat there feeling very homesick, the miner came home from work, had his traditional bath in front the fire and then sat down to an enormous supper. It was a hot day, and a wasp kept buzzing around him and it finally landed on the edge of his plate. With a quick stab the miner neatly squashed the wasp with his knife, flicked the remains on to the floor, wiped his knife on his trouser leg, and carried on eating with the knife as though nothing had happened."

The tester laughed. "They were tough in those places, I don't suppose your brother was used to that?"

"He certainly wasn't," Roger agreed, "but he soon got into the swing of the place. The good thing was the miner and his wife were kindness itself, and really made him feel at home." Roger carried on, "I went to visit him once or twice, the first time I found him, he was playing with a local gang about his own age, and all, including my brother were looking very grubby. They had just been having a stone fight with another gang, a popular past-time I was told. Now, I had a problem, because before I left Southwell, the bank manager's wife had made me put on my suit for the occasion, and I felt very conspicuous indeed when I met John and his gang."

"They took you as a toff," laughed the Tester.

"Exactly!" said Roger. "I stood there a bit tongue-tied, and the gang leader sized me up and down and said, "'Can he fight?' Not half," said my brother very loyally with great enthusiasm, and they accepted his word and after that we got on OK."

"Good question!" agreed the tester. "First things first for those lads".

"I took John to the pictures once," continued Roger, "and I shall never forget it. It was an "A" category film, and of course I was only twelve years old at the time, and John was only eight, but I was tall for my age and thought I could get by. I went up to the booking window and boldly asked for two tickets, one adult and one child, and the elderly lady behind the glass took my money and past over the tickets without demure. At the same time she was giving me the once over and said conversationally 'You *are* sixteen?' and I nodded. My dear brother, who was watching closely wasn't having this, and suddenly piped up in a shrill voice 'No you're not! You're only twelve!'"

The tester was very amused.

"Serve you right!" he laughed. "What happened then?"

"Well, the woman grabbed the tickets back in a flash, handed back my money and told me to go away. But we managed in the end," laughed Roger.

"How?"

"We just stood outside and badgered grown-ups coming in to 'please take us in,' and after a few minutes some friendly old man took pity on us and we went in with him".

The tester nodded in agreement "I remember doing that when I was a kid."

There was not much else to do for the moment, so Roger and the tester just sat there happily reminiscing over the war years. "I came down here in time for the bombing," said the Tester, and that was a serious business, but even that had a lighter side. There were many incidents to remember." and he paused for a chuckle. "I was on air-raid duty one night when Jerry plastered everywhere with incendiary bombs. One landed right up against our welding school hut which is the extension at the back of the Lab and next to our supply transformer. It lay there spluttering and about to burst into flame, and we rushed up and threw a bucket of sand over it. Mr Gallizia himself from the Rectifier Division was on duty with us, and he rushed up, wasn't satisfied, and bent right over the bomb, calling for more sand and packing it down with his hands. He was scared that it could set the whole area on fire, but somehow between us we managed to smother it and it just fizzled out and went dead."

"You were lucky," said Roger "we had some as well, and they were very difficult to put out."

"But you haven't heard the best bit yet," laughed the tester. "The headlines in the local morning paper told us that the bombs the night before had been a first off, they were special boobytrap incendiaries that also exploded! We all felt a bit green when we read that! We had our chuckles too," continued the tester. "We had a cartoon stuck up in the air-raid shelter which showed an air-raid in progress with bombs blowing houses to bits all around, and the cartoon showed below ground an air-raid shelter with a warden saying to some old ladies, 'Don't worry dears, you're as safe as houses down here!'

Roger laughed and joined in. "A nice one! I remember a story of when an air-raid warning had sounded in London, and everyone was rushing to the shelter in the Underground. Suddenly an old lady stopped, turned round, and started to totter back home. 'Where do you think you're going Granma?' asked the air raid warden. 'I've forgotten my teeth,' the old dear explained. 'Don't be daft!' said the warden, 'get down the shelter, you don't need your teeth, they're dropping bombs, not sandwiches!'"

Two weeks later, Roger moved into the welding hut as part of his training program. This was a busy place with the smell of smoke and hot iron very noticeable all the time. Two staff welders ran the hut for the apprentice training program in between being called out for any repair jobs in the factory. In the extended lunch hours, it was also quite common to find a surreptitious car pulled up round the back of the hut and a "foreigner" welding job being carried out to keep someone's "old banger" still road worthy. One frequent customer was an apprentice, who had an old Morgan three-wheeler that many said was past repairing, but being a keen lad, he was often there covered in rust and grease himself, borrowing a welding set and welding away on his own, confident that he could keep his precious vehicle hanging together for just a bit longer. "Part of my training," he would say.

After a brief introduction on welding, Roger was presented with a coloured shield to hold over his face to protect his eyes, and given an electric arc welding contraption. This contraption was simply a small holder in which was clamped a welding electrode rod, and joined by a thick cable to a hefty looking welding transformer. "This transformer is feeding you with several hundred amps of current at a very safe low voltage," he was told, "it is virtually indestructible; even when clumsy welders keep causing electrical short-circuits. A cut-out switch then turns off the current to protect the transformer, and you have to start your weld again. What you have done so far is then probably buggered!" With this minimum but succinct information, Roger was invited to try his first weld.

Roger started by striking the electrode tip on to a metal test sheet and immediately pulling the tip just off the surface to make an arc between the two. The exercise then was to draw the arc along the metal surface, keeping the arc burning evenly, and dragging out a consistent trough of molten metal in a long line with a crust of slag on the top. The metal electrode he was holding was melting away as he moved along, and the trick was to keep the tip of the electrode the same distance from the plate in order to keep a consistent arc burning. If you pulled away a little too far, the arc went out, and if you touched the plate, the electrodes stuck and the electric current tripped out. Roger found he could indeed keep a steady hand and was soon enjoying the exercise. "That's good!" complimented the instructor. "Have you done this before?"

"No, never!" answered Roger, "but I think I've got the hang of it."

"Just you wait and see," cautioned the instructor, "you haven't started yet!"

Roger was soon moved on to welding two strips of steel together at right angles, and Roger, by now getting quite adept at the technique, welded the two strips together in no time. He proudly presented the finished combined strip to the instructor who took one look, picked up a hammer, gave them a deft blow and the two strips fell apart and dropped to the floor.

The instructor stood there with a great grin on his face watching Roger's look of astonishment. "What did you do that for?" Roger managed to say at last.

"Because it was a crap weld," laughed the instructor.

"How do you mean?" asked Roger mortified.

The welder explained, "A weld has to be as strong if not stronger than the metal in the two pieces joined together, I only had to fart on your join and they fell apart!" Roger looked crestfallen. "Don't worry lad! Your problem was in going too fast and not dumping enough new metal into the join as you went along. You've also had a few jerks, and left lumps of slag buried in the join, look!" The instructor picked up the pieces and showed him his mistakes. He then added for good measure, "If this had been on a ship's hull, the damn thing would have sunk as soon as it was launched."

Roger got the message and had another go, being more careful and going slower, making sure there was plenty of molten metal flowing into the join and keeping his hands as steady as he possibly could. It took him a couple of days on quite a few strips before the instructor was satisfied.

Roger was also instructed in the art of much more delicate and expensive welding using an oxyacetylene blowtorch, and he found the principles were the same but it was very easy to apply too much flame and melt away the item that was supposed to be under repair. Practice however was very restricted in this technique because, he was told, the instructors' training budget would be over-spent in no time.

One day, an Outside Erection engineer came in, travelling slowly in his old Morris saloon with steam coming out from underneath the bonnet. The driver was in a very bad mood and his language was purple. He explained angrily, "I was down in South Wales in a fucking hurry as usual, and I flew round this bend, and there, right in front of me, was a stupid bloody sheep in the middle of the road. I did my best to stop, but I was still moving somewhat fast when I hit him fair and square, and the silly bugger went down like a nine-pin." He pointed. "As you can see, I've dented the bumper, buckled the wing a bit, and what's worse, I've sprung a leak in the radiator!" The welders and Roger stood around commiserating "I just stood there looking at my poor old car with the radiator leaking steam all over the place, and cursing the dead sheep lying in front of me," continued the engineer, "but then, you won't believe this, the bloody animal woke up, shook its head, rose unsteadily to its feet, and staggered off back into the field, leaving me alone with my wreckage!" Everyone in the welding school had gathered round by now and started laughing, and the engineer himself joined in. "It wasn't funny at the time, but everyone I tell the story to now starts laughing."

The welding instructors examined the car, "How did you get home?"

"Well, I've crawled back with a can of water to keep topping up the radiator, and I'm now hoping you can sort me out?"

"The dents and bends are easy," said the instructors nodding between themselves, "and we'll have a go at the radiator, it will be good training". They said this with a wink. Roger watched with admiration as the instructor carefully touched the leaks in the delicate copper honeycomb with the oxyacetylene flame, applying solder at the same time, and quite soon had the radiator repaired. "I think that will hold," they said cheerfully, and that will cost you a few beers."

They were always busy in the welding school, and there was great merriment one day when the apprentice with the Morgan rolled up once again, but this time on foot. "Where's your car?" asked the instructor. "Don't say you want some more welding?"

The apprentice shook his head sadly, "No, it's gone."

"Not another accident?" asked the instructor starting to grin.

"Worse than that," sighed the apprentice. "I was in Birmingham yesterday, in the front of a queue waiting at the traffic lights. When the lights went green, I put my foot down like I always do for a smart get-away, and my poor old Morgan broke into two!"

"What!" everyone exclaimed, "how do you mean?"

"The front half with the two wheels and the engine simply parted from the body and went skidding across the road, and I was left holding the disconnected steering wheel and sitting on the road in the back end of the car! I felt a proper fool, and the rest of the traffic all came to a stop!"

The instructors roared with laughter, "Are we surprised?" they laughed. "We told you last time that the old rust bucket was beyond repair."

"It was very embarrassing," continued the apprentice. "All the traffic came to a stop with laughing!"

"I bet they did, it's as good as they ever got in the old Keystone Cops silent movies."

"Thanks for nothing" said the apprentice, "I just thought I would let you know," and he trudged off on foot in the direction of the canteen.

CHAPTER 9

"Who's pinched my f..n' gloves?"

After his last two spells at Rectifiers and the laboratories, Roger really had no idea what to expect in his new assignment which was to the foundry. In his imagination he was seeing another very busy, noisy and dangerous place like the Big Shop, but with extras now of roaring bellows, furnaces, molten iron, and a general sort of mayhem thrown in. He remembered the blacksmith's shop at the end of the village green when he was a small boy. He used to stand at the door for ages, watching the furnace and the bellows, the constant noise of hammering, and the horses standing there patiently with a leg held backwards, and the sizzling smoke when the new horseshoe was pushed into position. Thus he was mildly surprised when he arrived to find the foundry here was reasonably peaceful, and a general air of quietly getting on with the job was the order of the day. There was the unmistakable heat and the smells of smoke and hot iron that he expected, but no hammering or roaring furnace to be heard anywhere!

Roger reported for duty, and a busy foreman sized him up and down and asked "Have you ever been around molten metal before?"

"Well no," said Roger, "but I have been through the welding lab, and seen small doses, but I don't suppose that counts here?"

"Hardly," smiled the foreman "but no matter, I always ask because it makes a difference to how we start you off. The first thing," he went on, "is to get yourself a pair of gloves from stores and for Christ's sake look after them. You will need them nearly all the time, and there's always someone who can't find his gloves at the critical time and start hollering out that someone has pinched 'em." Roger nodded. "And the most important thing is to always bear in mind that molten iron is extremely dangerous!" Roger grinned. "I can see you smirking," said the foreman sharply, "but when you handle the stuff all the time like we do here, it's very easy to start treating it like water, and then people get careless. Especially apprentices," he added with emphasis.

Roger smiled. "Sorry, I wasn't smirking," he said "but I can't imagine anyone mistaking molten iron for water!"

"Wait and see!" said the foreman, and led him to a staff member who was busy smoothing out sand in a shallow pit. "All your's Arthur," he said, and leaving Roger, he walked off.

Arthur stood up and greeted him with a smile. "Good!" he said. "You've come just right. I've got to cast a dozen bearing caps, and you can help me set up the moulds. We'll do three at a time as that's all I've got room for." Roger soon saw what was wanted. He was given the wooden pattern, a carefully modelled sturdy half- cylinder of wood, about an inch thick and a foot long, with flanges on each side and ribs on the outside. Roger looked at it carefully, and was told to press it down, bulge upwards, into a metal box full of sand, then very carefully lift it out, and study the impression left in the sand. Arthur was watching him closely, "You must make sure that the sand impression is absolutely perfect, no gaps."

Roger grinned, "this is just like making sand-castles on the beach," he said."

Exactly," grunted Arthur peering at Roger's handiwork. "That's OK, now put the pattern back over the sand, and press down this second box of sand on top very carefully in order to get the top side impression, once again, without any gaps" Roger did as he was bid, and Arthur then continued "Now comes the tricky bit. We must very carefully lift the top box off, it's a special sand mixture that will stick in position, and check that the top impression is as perfect as the bottom." Roger again followed, and they both peered at the final impressions, a nice clean replica in sand of both the inside and outside of the pattern. "That's fine" said Arthur, and proceeded to make a small hole in the top mould out to the top of the box where there was a funnel opening. "That's where we pour in the metal" he explained. "Now, take the pattern out and put the top back on, very, very, gently and this one will be ready for casting" Once again, Roger followed the instruction successfully, and Arthur produced some bolts and locked the two halves together. "That looks OK," he said. "Now have a go at the next two yourself, and I will check them before you put the two halves together. When that's done we shall be ready to cast."

Roger carried on very carefully and finally, with the help of Arthur adding the pour holes, all three moulds were soon sitting side by side in the sand ready for casting. Roger had noticed other staff working with different patterns in their own areas of sand, and admired the speed and deftness with which they were working. He felt he was very slow in comparison, but Arthur had said nothing. "Good!" said Arthur at last, "I suppose you want to see the casting business now?"

"Yes, I can't wait," said Roger eagerly.

"Right, then put your gloves on and come over here."

Against the back wall in the middle of the foundry stood the furnace, a large, tall container heavily insulated on the outside with, near the bottom, a hole covered with slag and a trough underneath from which molten iron could obviously be drained off. As they approached Roger could feel the heat, and he realised that he was indeed getting hot himself and starting to sweat. "This is an electric furnace." explained Arthur, "it is running all day when we are working, and we tap the iron off ourselves when we are ready, it's always bloody hot, very nice in the winter, but the whole place gets like an oven in the summer." He lifted up a large cast iron bucket with a handle and a big spout and placed it under the trough end, and proceeded to call up the overhead crane. As the crane trundled up, Arthur turned to Roger. "Once we drain off our iron, we've got to move quickly as the damn stuff will start to set if we hang about, so we have to make sure that we're absolutely ready before we start."

"OK!" said Roger, "I understand that."

"Good!" grunted Arthur and he adjusted the crane and hooked it on the bucket. He then picked up a long pole kept at the side of the furnace, and knocked at the slag covering the drain hole at the bottom. He had to knock hard several times, and suddenly Roger found himself catching his breath as a stream of molten iron came pouring down the trough into Arthur's bucket. Arthur stood there watching and half shielding his face from the heat, and when he had poured enough he rammed a big lump of a clay mixture he had ready into the hole and the flow stopped. Roger found his eyes glued to the bucket, it seemed impossible that iron could be poured like this, and yet here it was, slopping around in the bucket, a fiery red liquid glowing with an ever-changing iridescent surface and giving out its own heat which Roger could feel from where he stood. "Come on!" shouted Arthur, and they followed the bucket now swinging gently on the crane until they were back over their own patch.

Roger stood back and watched the final manoeuvring as Arthur picked up a special lever which fitted the bucket, and guided the bucket over their moulds. He then gently tipped up the bucket over the pour holes and Roger watched fascinated as he deftly poured the molten iron into their moulds one by one until they were full. "Just like pouring out a cup of tea," thought Roger and he could see what the foreman had said about water!

"Good, that's that!" grunted Arthur wiping his brow, and signalled to the crane driver to take the bucket away. Roger watched the nearly empty bucket sail away to where a gadget on top of the furnace now took the bucket and tipped what was left of the molten iron back into the top of the furnace. "If we don't get that bucket back before the rest of the iron sets, we get a real bollocking," commented Arthur as he stood beside him. "Right!" continued Arthur "Now we get to your bit."

"What's that?" asked Roger who was very entranced with the whole business so far.

"As soon as the moulds are cool enough to touch, I want you to knock out the new bearing caps we've cast, brush all the sand off them, have a careful look at the edges and the pour hole spots, and file off any bits of excess iron so that we end up with smooth professional jobs."

"OK," said Roger, although inwardly he groaned. "I thought I'd finished filing after Big Shop," he said to himself. "Once again, we apprentices get all the rotten jobs!"

The next few days flew by, and, on the whole, Roger enjoyed the work. The most satisfying time was after the iron in the mould had set, and the box was open and the new casting tipped out on to the sand. This was carried out as soon as possible, whilst the casting was still far too hot to hold with bare hands and Roger realised that without gloves all the work would be considerably slowed down. Nevertheless, he noticed some of the old hands seem to have asbestos fingers, and often picked up pieces with a quick snatch and blow on their fingers when they couldn't be bothered with gloves. "Don't you try this son!" an elderly worker said to him, "or you'll end up with horny old hands like mine," and he grinned and showed Roger his browned and extremely leathery looking fingers. "I have to put gloves on every night when I get in bed with the missus," he said grinning, and his two neighbours heard him and interrupted with loud guffaws.

"Don't listen to him son!" they shouted. "He's only boasting again."

Roger grinned and made a mental note to keep a careful watch on his own gloves, bearing in mind the foreman's initial warning. "How right he was!" he thought.

Roger realised a few days later that he had a rather embarrassing little problem, he had developed a verruca on his one of his feet and it

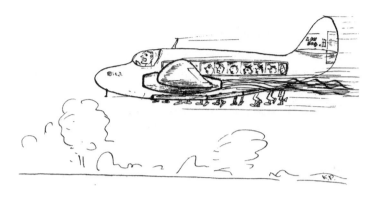

"...and start running as soon as we touch down."

wasn't responding to a number of ointments he applied. In final exasperation, he decided to pop over to the Medical Centre for advice. Roger was always a very healthy person and considered visiting a doctor only one step from the grave. He went on a Monday morning, fresh from a Sunday night bath, and the doctor peered at the verruca and grinned at Roger's worried face. "Don't worry, you won't die" he said, "but this is a big juicy verruca, you've left it alone rather too long, and we'll have to burn it out."

"OK!" nodded Roger, "When?"

"I'll start now" said the doctor, "but you'll have to come back twice a week for a few weeks until we've cleared it up." The doctor was as good as his word, and after watching a quite painless operation, Roger went back to the foundry with a light heart and a neat plaster on the sole of his foot. "Come back Thursday," reminded the doctor as Roger departed.

Roger walked back chuckling. The doctor had reminded him of a silly joke he remembered, told him years ago by his dad. "A doctor was visiting a wounded soldier in hospital, and the soldier was in quite a bad way. 'Doctor! doctor,' he had cried, 'will I die?' 'Nonsense' the doctor had replied 'that's the last thing you will do.'" Roger smiled at the memory; his dad was always full of little quips. Roger remembered once, long before the war, walking across the village green with him, and Roger was watching a small biplane high above them making heavy weather against a strong westerly wind. In fact, it didn't seem to be making any progress at all. Roger was quite young at the time, and he asked "dad! that aeroplane isn't moving."

His dad without even looking up had replied "It's OK, the pilot's just popped out for a cup of tea." Roger remembered how he didn't say anything at the time, but had worried for weeks where the tea had come from, and why the pilot hadn't fallen out the sky.

Come Thursday, Roger was on his way back to the Medical Centre as planned, when he suddenly thought about his feet. He had forgotten all about his verruca. He had not been near a bath since the Sunday, and he realised his feet might be grubby. He hurried into the nearest toilet, took his "toe-tector" and his sock off, and realised that the plaster had long gone and sure enough, his foot was covered in black grime from the foundry floor. There was no time to do much, so he hastily put his foot in the hand basin, rinsed his foot as clean as he could, put his sock and boot back on and hurried off to his appointment. As he walked into the Medical Centre, he realised that the other foot would be just as dirty which he hadn't washed. "Too late now," he thought, and carried on hoping and praying that the doctor or a nurse wouldn't ask to check the other foot. Roger's luck held, and for the next three weeks he continued to wash just the one foot clean every time before his appointments.

One day, a couple of apprentices came into the foundry, made straight for Arthur, and said "Arthur! We've a little foreigner we need to do. Is it OK?"

Arthur grinned at the two, "I thought you had enough of us when you were with us? What is it this time?"

The two lads looked around to check the foreman was not there and explained. "It is the apprentices' Christmas Ball next week, and we have decided to put up a nice centrepiece for the occasion. We want to cast it to make something special, look, here you are." And they unwrapped a large paper parcel and produced a lavatory seat.

"What the bloody hell's that?" exploded Arthur, his eyes bulging out of his head.

"It's a lavatory seat "grinned the spokesman, "haven't you see one before?"

"I can see that you silly bugger!" exclaimed Arthur "Don't be so bloody clever. What I mean is, what the hell do you want to mess about casting a bog seat for? Haven't you anything better to do?"

Roger had realised earlier that Arthur was the man who was always very popular with the apprentices and obviously enjoyed their confidences over anything special. This time, however, he looked really stunned. "But you can get bog seats two a penny anywhere, you don't have to mess about casting one. What the hell's getting into you all?"

"It's for a joke," explained the spokesman "We make a point of something different every Christmas Ball, and we plan to have a lot of fun with this."

"You're crazy" grunted Arthur, but however, he peered at the lavatory seat with his professional eye. "Well, it makes a simple pattern. With what I've taught you, you should have no difficulty with it. Wait till the lunch hour and have a go at it yourselves. I'm not even going to look!"

"Old Arthur's feeling shy!" one apprentice grinned to the other.

"Bugger off!" said Arthur doing his best not to laugh, "hide the dam thing over there for now and come back at one o'clock."

Roger was very curious to see how the apprentices would manage on their own, but he need not have worried. They came back as planned, made their mould easily and competently, fetched their own molten iron, and had quite soon poured the job. Roger stood watching, "Roger!" said one of them straightening up "Can we borrow your gloves?"

Roger stepped forward happily, "I thought you had forgotten," and laughed. "Keeping gloves handy was the first thing I was taught."

"No one forgets that," smiled the apprentice, and in about ten minutes after pouring, the iron was set and they knocked it out of the mould. They stood looking at their, still extremely hot, handiwork with quiet satisfaction.

"Very good!" said Arthur right behind them, and they jumped round in surprise. Arthur had been surreptitiously watching all the time, and he now came forward with several other staff who had picked up what was going on. "You've made quite a nice job there! Well done." The group stood around looking, and a general guffaw spread among them.

"Sod me!" said one "what will they get up to next?"

"No telling" answered another "but they'd better not sit down on this for a bit, they'll burn their arse off."

"We don't keep gloves for arses," said a third and they all stood their laughing. "But who would sit on the damn thing when it's cold?"

"Only a poor bugger with burning piles" came the answer, "he might be grateful!" and with considerable merriment they returned to their own patches .

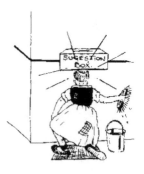

Arthur, however, had the last word. "You had better get the dam thing out of here as soon as you can," he said. "One of these days you'll get me into real trouble." He paused and stared at the seat. "I still can't see what the hell you're going to do with it. You can't swap it for an ordinary bog seat anywhere, it'll be quite heavy! Someone would drop the thing down and shatter the pan!"

"Leave it to us," grinned the apprentices, "and thanks for your help," and they hid the seat in a corner and came back and collected it at quitting time.

Arthur, still grinning turned to Roger and shook his head "Anything to do with lavatories is always a source of humour to you young buggers. It must be something that gets into your blood at a very early age!"

"Nonsense, it's universal" laughed Roger, "I can tell you a true story that is slightly indelicate but invariably gets a good laugh, even from our very proper mother when we first told her."

"Go on then," grinned Arthur.

"This story is absolutely true and happened on the top field of the nursery one day. My younger brother and our cousin, who were always up to mischief when together, would often join the men dung-turning, a regular job when preparing new mushroom beds. The foreman with them was an old retainer named Fred Wright who had developed a habit of relieving himself in mid-morning without walking all the way down the hill to where the offices were. Instead, he would just retire to a corner of the hedge where he was well hidden, drop his trousers, squat down, do the necessary and be back at work in a jiffy."

Arthur was grinning from ear to ear already.

"I know, everyone laughs!" said Roger. "Now, all the men and the two boys knew of this habit of old Fred's and normally took no notice, but this day, for a dare, the two lads hid behind the hedge, and as old Fred did his usual, they caught the whole load on a shovel they had silently slipped underneath him as he squatted down. Old Fred was very deaf, and that made the task much easier!" Both Roger and Arthur were by now laughing. "Poor old Fred" chuckled Roger "he stood up when he had finished, and by now the shovel had been deftly pulled back out of site, and when he turned round to admire his handiwork there was nothing there!" Arthur now laughed out loud as Roger continued. "Fred just stood there looking stunned. He poked around in the grass with a stick looking for his 'offering,', and finally took his trousers off to study them inside as well but to no avail! He was still shaking his trousers looking more and more worried where he noticed that all the men were creasing themselves laughing, and of course he then discovered what was going on. I told you, you would laugh," said Roger, and they both went back to work, still chuckling.

"That reminds me of an old saying of my uncle's," finished Roger. "He used to say that one boy on his own would do the work of a man, two boys together would do the work of half a man, and three boys together would get no work done at all!"

"He was bloody right!" agreed Arthur.

This would be Roger's second Christmas in the factory, and he remembered the year before how the place had slowly ground to a halt halfway through the morning of Christmas Eve, and by mid afternoon, only a few stalwarts with bad heads were left to make their way home. He had been in Big Shop at the time, and he had expressed his surprise to his workmates when bottles of beer were suddenly produced well before lunch time.

"It's tradition," he was told, "There won't be much work done today, it's Christmas!" and Roger had noticed the same attitude everywhere. "The bloody offices are the worst," he was told "You should see the state of some of those staff by lunch time. What's good for the goose is good for the gander," explained a cheerful fitter "I've been in several factories over the past few years, and it's the same everywhere on Christmas Eve. It's tradition!" This seemed to be an absolute justification and Roger happily joined in with the mood.

This Christmas was just the same, and Roger was rather stunned when an apprentice came into the foundry, came up to Arthur and said in an attitude of considerable satisfaction "Arthur, 'I've just done it!"

"What's that" several around asked, noticing the lad's rather excited nature.

"I've been in Q shop" the lad blurted out.

"That was asking for trouble," said Arthur, "we all keep well away from there, especially at Christmas time. It's a girl's-only department, they're a rough lot, and they have been known to get you young lads in there, debag you and smother your bits with soot! I thought you would have known that?"

"I know" laughed the lad, "but my room-mates dared me to go in as it was Christmas Eve."

"More fool you!" said Arthur.

"Oh it was OK" continued the lad "I walked in, and the girls surrounded me and said 'Get 'em off!'. Well, so I said 'OK, I will if one of you will do the same!' And blow me! one of the girls did just that, in front of us all. Well, then I had to follow of course, and in no time I was also standing there as naked as she was. And guess what? We did it!" he said with a sound of triumph in his voice.

"You mean.." started Arthur.

"Why not try the dartboard?"

"Yes we did it!" interrupted the lad in triumph. "It was my first time," and he paused and sat down, leaning backwards with smug satisfaction all over his face. "It was great!" He suddenly added. "I shall do that again!" There was a sort of stunned silence all round.

"Have a drop of my beer," said Arthur slowly, "this takes the fuckin' biscuit."

By early afternoon, the furnace had been switched off, and there was a general air of "laissez-faire" in the foundry, and all the staff were getting ready to go home. "It's nowhere near closing time yet!" Roger pointed out, but he was met with a derisory laugh.

"Don't be daft son!" came the reply "It's Father Christmas on the gate this afternoon, and he'll be glad to see the back of us. Have a look outside." The foundry was near the canal gate, and when Roger looked out he could already see a steady trickle of workers already making their way home, past a very happy looking works' policeman. He was exchanging jokes and with many he knew, and a generally cheerful repartee was the order of the day.

Suddenly, out of the blue, one of Roger's slight acquaintances, a senior sales manager named Ken Starr came into the foundry. He was based in the South African office, and home on a month's Christmas leave. He grabbed Roger in a most jovial manner. "Come on Roger, it's time to get you back to the Hall. There's nothing else going to be done here today. I've got a hired car and I'll take you there." The manager had lunched in the senior dining room because of his status, and Roger could see that he was looking rather the worse for wear.

"Had a good lunch?" he asked, more in sarcasm than interest, and Ken burst into laughter.

"I should say so! We had champagne to kick off with, several bottles of 'Chateau Neuf du Pap' during the meal, and we sat round with the traditional port and stilton to finish." He paused and rubbed his stomach lovingly. "Half of them are still there, waiting for transport to take them home," he laughed, "but they're in no hurry."

"I'd better go with him to make sure he's OK," thought Roger. He himself had downed a few beers in the canteen over lunch, and was feeling very happy himself and quite glad to have an excuse for a ride back. He had anticipated problems that day, had left his bike behind and had come in on the works' bus. "But goodness knows when that will leave today," he thought, so he gladly accepted the manager's offer.

It was a curious journey. The sales manager was very conscious of the drink inside him, and proceeded to crawl all the six miles back though the city in either first or second gear only. "You can't be too careful!" he explained cheerfully to Roger, "I wouldn't want to cause an accident." Roger sat beside him feeling very aware of the queues of frustrated cars behind them half the time, but felt it safer to just sit quiet, hold on tight to his seat, and say nothing.

There were repeated honks from horns behind them, and when occasionally a car managed to get past, the driver would give them an angry stare as he sped away. Roger shrunk back in his seat, feeling dreadful and hoping the world would swallow him up, but Ken was totally oblivious to the mayhem. "It was the same last time I was home," he reminisced cheerfully. "On Christmas Eve the roads are full of drivers coming home from work early with a skin full. It's disgraceful really, you just have to be very careful, keep a sharp eye open, and avoid them." Roger kept his peace, sitting quietly with growing embarrassment as Ken seemed to get slower and slower. They finally reached the Hall in one piece, and Roger breathed a sigh of relief. He reckoned the last two miles had been totally in first gear.

Roger's embarrassment was not yet over. Ken insisted in coming into the Hall with him where they met the apprentice supervisor's wife, Mrs Rollason, trying to feed her young son in a children's highchair. It was the child's awkward age, and there was mushy food all over his face. Ken strode over to her, the cold air after the hot car was having an effect. "Good evening mishush Rollashon," he managed to say with an effort. "May I wishhh you the complimentsh of the sheashon!" Poor Mrs Rollason looked startled, but before she could respond, Ken started to apologise, "I am afraid I am not shpeaking too shucshinctyl" he said carefully, "it mushed be the heavy luncshh." He turned round to Roger, very amused with himself. "Shucshinctly" he said and tried again. "Shucshincty."

"I think you had better sit down and have a cup of tea," said Mrs Rollason kindly, but Ken politely said he couldn't stop and wobbled back to his car, occasionally muttering "Shucshinctly," to himself with a slight giggle as he went. "He hasn't got much further to go thank goodness," said the concerned Mrs Rollason, "but I expect he will be alright, salesmen are pretty resilient."

Roger met the same manager a few days later back at work "How are you? did you get home OK on Christmas Eve?" Roger asked.

"Of course I did. Why do you ask?" Ken replied looking surprised "Well, you were "shuctshinctly" under the weather when you left the Hall!" said Roger imitating.

"Oh that", he laughed dismissively. "I was OK as soon as I got home, but," he added, "there was a bit of bother later that day in the works"

"What was that? "asked Roger.

"About six o'clock, a father phoned up the main gate and said he was worried because his daughter, who works at the factory, had not come home." He continued, "By then the factory was all closed up, offices locked and only the night works police on duty," "Well," said Roger, "I expect she had gone somewhere with her pals."

"No" he said, "the father had phoned up one of her office friends who said the she believed her friend might still be up in the office because there had been a few drinks, 'just a few' she said, but the last thing she remembered was her friend feeling quite sick!"

Roger was aghast, "What happened?"

Ken carried on. "Well, the gate policeman got the keys, went up to the office which was of course dark and getting cold, and there the girl was, quite alright, but sound asleep on the floor. The father had also come in and was with the police when they found his daughter. I gather he is now raising hell over the matter, and there is a big enquiry to be held."

"I'm not surprised!" said Roger, "that's the worst story I've heard."

"Before I met you on Christmas Eve," continued Ken, "I had been talking to that German consultant engineer, Doctor Friedlander who joined us just before the war.

"I know him" said Roger, he is a wonderful man, and has helped me more than once."

"Well", laughed Ken, "He had been telling me about the different attitude to work between us and the Germans. He said Germans were always at their desks promptly at the start, and never dreamt of even slowing down before the closing time. He himself carried on the same habits when he joined us, and many had remarked about his strict self-discipline."

"I know" said Roger, "when he saw me he just got immersed in the problem I had gone to see him about, and didn't stop discussing it with me until the 5.18 bell went when he made his excuses and went home. In the mornings, I have often seen him wobbling in on his bicycle, always precisely about ten minutes before start time."

"That's him," said Ken, " but he told me he was worried about the poor timing he saw in England, particularly time off for tea breaks, extended lunch hours, late starting, and the universal habit of packing up before the closing bell went."

"I don't suppose it makes all that much difference," said Roger "What do you think?"

Ken hardly paused. "Not a lot I'm sure," he said, "but," and he paused to have a chuckle, "as it was Christmas Eve, I said to the good Doctor, 'You have seen nothing yet,' and I took him for a walk around some of the shop floors and offices."

"I bet he was surprised," said Roger.

"He was more than surprised, he was absolutely astounded. When we had finished, he turned to me shook his head, and said sadly, 'Mister Starr, I am afraid your country will never compete with Germany now Europe is recovering from the war!'"

Ken turned to go away, but stopped and suddenly asked, "By the way, what happened to the iron lavatory seat that you apprentices cast in the foundry?"

Roger grinned. "We had our fun with that all right! On the big night of the Christmas Ball, it appeared as a centrepiece in our decorated entrance hall. It had been painted with several coats of black enamel, and was hung up with an enlarged photo of our boss, Mr Rollason, in the middle of it. Underneath it was a notice saying, 'The seat of all learning.'"

Ken laughed, "I like that! What was the reaction?"

"It was good, Rolly laughed himself, and several of our Management guests had a hard look at it and complimented Rolly on the excellence of the casting."

"Good for you!" laughed Ken.

"But it didn't stop there," continued Roger. "When we all sat down for supper, the seat disappeared. Some of the lads lifted it down and took it to the lavatory earmarked 'Ladies only' for the night. They nipped in there, unscrewed the existing seat, placed our casting on the pan, and propped the old lid up behind it. Then they swopped the light bulb for a forty watt to make the room dimmer, and escaped without being spotted."

"Go on!" said Ken grinning from ear to ear.

"What do you expect?" laughed Roger, "after supper there was a queue for the 'ladies', we had the usual contingent from the nurses hostel with us, and at least half a dozen took their turn in the loo before the alarm was raised. The whole exercise had been a last minute rush as usual, and it turned out that the black enamel wasn't quite dry, and after it warmed up someone stuck to the pan!"

"Oh my God!" cried Ken holding his sides laughing, "I don't want to hear any more!" and he went off shaking his head and grinning from ear to ear.

CHAPTER 10

"If it works, don't fix it!"

Poole Power Station

Roger was getting near the end of his two years as an apprentice, and was looking forward to his next post very much. The posting was to Outside Erection, where several of his colleagues were already working, and they had given him repeated tales of crises and disasters neatly avoided by the hard core of the permanent staff. It was generally understood that this army of skilled engineers, spread throughout the world, spent their whole lives cheerfully wrestling with impossible time demands, awkward customers, new equipment not quite working as planned, and, as one engineer had put it, "We are the living proof of Sod's law, if anything can possibly go wrong it will! It governs every dam job we do!" However, despite the problems, Roger had heard nothing from the apprentices but praise and enjoyment for the time spent in the posting, and he reported for duty with high expectations.

Outside Erection had no offices of their own, but spent their time either on customer sites, or liaising with test or design departments in the factory. Thus, Roger was instructed to report to the chief of Turbo-generator Design where, as he walked across to their offices, he had a sudden foreboding of what he would be involved in. He was right, the chief looked at him and welcomed him into his office. "I'm glad you are free," he started off. "Do you remember the work you did for us in helping to resolve our voltage regulator stability problems for the Poole power station generators?" Roger remembered vividly, he had sat for days stewing over some modern American technical papers, until the penny had dropped and he had prepared the equations to settle the details of the control circuits.

"Yes Sir!" said Roger, "I remember very well, we had to take the final equations down to the National Physics Laboratory for them to solve on their new electronic computer."

"That's it," beamed the chief "Well, you will be pleased to know that we have used your equations ever since, and we are getting a lot of praise for the performances we are getting."

"That's good news!" smiled Roger, but with a cold feeling in his stomach. "What was coming next!" he thought to himself. He didn't consider himself an expert on the subject and felt rather inadequate, but he continued, smiling bravely "I felt in the end I had got to the bottom of the requirements, it's good to hear they are standing up to real use."

"More than that," continued the chief, "we have now been asked by the Central Electricity Generating Board to put the system to the ultimate test!"

Roger's heart sunk. "What could he mean?" The Chief continued carefully, "The Board have asked whether our system will permit a generator to carry on running on the National Grid Network for a few seconds if the excitation system fails. We have so much confidence now in the system that we have said 'Yes', and a series of important tests are being organised on one of our generators in the new power station in Poole harbour."

Roger knew exactly what the tests would involve, and why it was important. The excitation was the system that supplied a large magnetising current to the massive great rotor spinning at fifty revolutions per second. Without the powerful pull from the magnetic effect of the rotor, the speed of the rotor would be uncontrolled, and unless emergency action was taken, the rotor would simply keep accelerating, driven by the high steam pressure from the boiler system until an explosion would occur which would wreck the plant completely. Roger swallowed. "That sounds very dangerous?" he ventured.

The chief laughed, "We wouldn't stay without excitation for long of course," he explained, "but long enough to take detailed recordings of exactly what goes on inside the generator, and whether restoration of the excitation can actually stop the acceleration and pull the set back into synchronism."

Roger thought hard. "I guess it might, but I'm not certain. My calculations didn't cover any uncontrolled acceleration. But what about the forces inside the generator?" he asked, "The calculations showed you would get a total short circuit inside the machine every time it slipped a magnetic pole!"

"We've checked that," the chief re-assured him. "Thanks to your equations, we now believe we shall be OK. We shall of course, take the tests very carefully, starting on a no-load trial, and gradually building up to a full load test as we go along. That is unless we get any nasty surprises on the way."

The chief sat back in his chair waiting for Roger to respond, but he suddenly added, "Both us and the Board will gain from the tests. We and the Board will gain technical proof that the machines can handle a dangerous condition, and the Board need to know this in order to finalise their operating room procedures. At the moment, the very idea of slipping a magnetic pole when on load fills them with fear and trembling."

"Me too" thought Roger to himself, but he held his peace, and thought for a moment. "Who else will be there?" he asked cautiously.

"Don't worry, I shall be there myself of course" smiled the chief, "the senior erection engineer, several lads making the recording, and," he pointed at Roger, "that will include you, and an army of Central

Electricity Generating Board staff, including the station super. You won't be on your own! But you!" smiled the chief "will be our 'brain box' on site, and you will get plenty of grilling from the CEGB staff and the consultant engineers."

Roger felt reassured and alarmed at the same time. "Still," he thought, "in for a penny, in for a pound." So he swallowed hard and carried on. "Fine!" he said "When will we start?"

"This week," said the chief standing up. "If it's OK with you we want you to go home and pack your overnight gear in a bag. Someone from Erection will pick you up before lunch, and take you down to Poole. We expect to start the actual test runs by Wednesday, and get home for the weekend."

"They don't hang about here!" thought Roger to himself and went back to the Hall to get ready.

As planned, a young Scotsman in a fast sports car rolled up at the Hall mid-morning and introduced himself. "Howdee!" he grinned, "Are you Roger the lodger the brain box?" he asked.

"Why, yes, my name is Roger," he admitted cautiously, "but.."

" "Good!" the newcomer interrupted. "My name's George, we can talk while we travel. Pop in, and we'll be off." He held the passenger door open, flung Roger's little case into the back and invited Roger to step in "It's a bit of a squeeze" he said "but we shall get there OK. I want to hurry and get there before dark to start the wiring of the recorders tonight." Roger looked around the tiny car. Every spare inch was stuffed with boxes holding penrecorders, meters, rolls of wire, a large hold-all full of tools, and a large cloth bundle in the front of Roger's feet. "Sorry about the squeeze," he said. "You can't hurt that bundle, that's my own bits and pieces and it's mainly a few spare clothes. So sit tight and we'll be off" It was immediately obvious to Roger that here was a cheerful, no nonsense, thoroughly self confident engineer who would not suffer fools gladly. He seemed only a few years older than Roger and yet he seemed to have all the confidence in the world, Roger hoped that one day he would feel like him, but he felt there was still a long way to go!

George set off at a cracking pace, and as soon as they left the city he seemed, to Roger, to start driving like a lunatic. George however, was in his element "We've got about a hundred and eighty miles to go and about six hours daylight left," he calculated, taking his eyes off the road and glancing at his wrist watch, "so it will be easy. The snag with power stations," he added, "is that once the day-time staff go home, the places get shut like a bloody tomb, and it takes loads of red tape to get past security. He turned to Roger while still driving along at the same pace and started a friendly conversation as though they were sitting in armchairs round the fire. "I've been told that you are a bit of a boffin?" he enquired.

"No not at all!" said Roger hastily. "I just did a bit of research into voltage regulators, the maths came out OK, and now I suppose I've got a bit of a reputation over it. But I've only done some testing work in Main Test, I've never been in a power station in my life."

George laughed "Don't worry, I'm sure the Design Office know what they are doing, and you'll be in good company. It's called in the trade "The blind leading the blind." We are all experts at it!" and George chuckled to himself as he flew round another couple of tight bends. However, Roger couldn't really concentrate; he was too busy holding on to his seat with his eyes glued to the road.

They flew round another corner and the road was partly blocked in front. Before Roger could hardy blink, George had slammed on the brakes, slowed right down, and steered easily past the obstruction without turning a hair. Roger then realised that George had much quicker reactions than his own, and was obviously comfortable at the speed they were going. Not so Roger, and after a few further desultory sentences, Roger decided to leave the driving to George, so he shut his eyes and dropped off to sleep as the least alarming option. George was not the least put out, and most of the rest of the journey was carried out in a companionable silence.

They finally came hurtling into Poole as it was getting dusk. As they rounded the last bend, Roger saw the power station for the first time with its tall chimneys looming up out of the mist. Roger felt his lips tightening at the sight and a sharp knot started crawling around in his stomach. "Right! this is it!" he thought. "If the maths aren't proved correct now, and it all goes wrong, I don't know what I'll do."

George however was in the best of spirits, "Good!" he said. "Made it! We'll still catch the day shift before they go home, wake 'em all up, and get the show started. They won't be at all pleased at having to wait before they get their evening slippers on." With a cheerful laugh he came to a stop and they had arrived! Roger immediately felt better.

When they made themselves known, they found two engineers waiting for them, and together all the contents at the back of George's car were soon carried up and spread out on the turbine floor. There were six bulky pen recorders, a whole pile of meters, several untidy heaps of connecting cables, and a little mountain of fresh paper rolls for the recorders. Not to mention the basic essentials of insulating tape, simple sticky tape, ink cartridges, plasticine, scribbling paper, a heap of pencils and extension leads for portable telephones. Finally George brought up his large toolbox, and threatened anyone who touched it with instant death. "What an untidy mess" thought George "just like being at home in Main Test." The rest of the turbine floor, which seemed to stretch for miles in this great tall building, was impeccably clean!

Most of the team were considerably senior to Roger, but there was an air of total companionship and confidence between them all, and Roger began to feel fully relaxed and actually looking forward to the tests. By Wednesday night everything was ready and they were all suffering from lack of sleep. They had stayed up half of Monday and Tuesday nights and were all feeling distinctly bleary eyed. "It's always like this," muttered George, "I don't know any damn job where we have managed to stick to decent hours." George, however was an old hand, nothing would upset him. "We are all a bit bushed," he said to the assembled team. "There's nothing more to do tonight, we start tests tomorrow, so how about going out for a beer and a night off?" There was unanimous agreement to such an excellent suggestion, also fully endorsed by the two senior consultants, so off they all trouped to a nearby pub. Roger felt that no doubt this was a very common practise!

After a few drinks there was a curious incident that Roger remembered for years afterwards. There was a cinema close by advertising a new Kenneth More film called *Time Flies*, a comedy. The whole team, now about six strong, plus the two consulting engineers all decided to go and see the film. The cinema was nearly empty, and as they went in, their timing was lucky as the main film was just starting, and all the title introductory screens were still in progress. These opening shots were shown to a background of ascending balloons, hundreds of them. The team, sitting bleary-eyed but comfortable with the warm feeling of the beers inside, were watching this opening sequence which seemed to be going on and on, and they all peered silently at this steady stream of balloons rising behind the titles. Suddenly, one of the team said in a very load voice, "This is a load of balls!" and all the team started to giggle. As these title shots and the balloons went on and on, the giggles broke into guffaws, and then into quite hysterical laughter, Roger included, and they found themselves rolling around in their seats, quite helpless with laughter. No one knew afterwards quite why it had seemed so funny, perhaps it was their near exhaustion? Anyhow, no-one threw them out, and indeed, it was a good film and they all left afterwards quite refreshed and looking forward to the next day.

All the team were staying in the same hotel and, before retiring, a nightcap was the order of the day. As they sat supping, George said, "We had a real good laugh in the Design Office yesterday."

"What's new!" said one of the consultants, "you all seem to be laughing half the time!"

"Ah, this was a very strange one," said George. "We have a large five thousand horsepower DC mine-winding motor in a South African gold mine, where there had been overload problems needing repairs to the commutator. The Company is Anglo- American, and they were furious about the hold-up to their output schedule. Now Anglo-American is one of our biggest customers outside the UK, and when their overseas director phones us up, we jump!" He paused to take a long drink from his glass. Roger had to admire his drinking capacity! George then continued. "Well, Anglo insisted that our head of the design team should go out to Johannesburg personally to supervise the repairs and our management agreed."

"Was that really necessary?" queried a listener.

"Course it wasn't," snorted George. "We have staff out there could do the job with no problems, but when Anglo say 'jump', we jump! So the designer in question, poor old Alec, had to pack at a moment's notice and fly out. Now, what we are all laughing about is the fact that Alec had never been abroad in his life before, and the whole office complimented him on his luck. All sorts of suggestions flew round the office about all the interesting things he could do out there, including of course going on safari and seeing real wild animals and so on. He was also given a list of souvenirs to bring back. He even bought himself a new camera, and his wife thoughtfully helped with a load of extra strong sun cream.

"Sounds like a holiday!" said a consultant.

"No chance," laughed George. "That's the joke. When he arrived in Jo'burg it was after dark, there was an Anglo-American car waiting for him, and they drove along dusty dirt tracks for the next two hours before arriving at the mine. The winding motor was two thousand feet down at the inter-mediate mine level, and he was taken straight down underground where he stayed for the next three days. They had sleeping bunks and food down there at the winder level. When the repair was finished, up he came to the surface where, would you believe it, it was getting dark again, and they drove him straight back to catch a night flight home. So, after all that, he never even saw daylight in South Africa before he was on his way home again!" With a general laugh all round, the assembled company retired to be ready for the next day.

The day of the tests arrived and Roger found himself pushed into the limelight in front of the station supervisor himself, together with senior levels of the CEGB staff covering the civil, the electrical and the mechanical heads of department. It was a long meeting and took most of the morning. Roger found himself repeating all the explanations of his mathematics, and the chief of design sat at his side giving him wholehearted support by re-assuring customer and the consultants that we all knew exactly what we were doing. Extra CEGB staff had arrived from London headquarters and Roger was pleased to hear one of them had also studied the American technical papers that Roger had used, and he gave qualified support for the tests.

The tests started after lunch, the first one being with hardly any electricity power output from the generator, but nevertheless the noise of the combined steam turbine and generator was very un-nerving as Roger and the team stood by its side on the turbine floor. The set was already connected to the National Grid system, and Roger realised that they would now be supplying electricity to the whole Poole district. He prayed silently that nothing would go wrong. They checked all the recorders; they all seemed to be working and the signal was given for the first test. As the excitation current was removed, the generator slowly drifted out of step with the National Grid, suddenly there was a sharp "WOOF" from the system. This was the pole slip that Roger had dreaded as the magnetising restraint died away, and Roger felt a tremor beneath his feet from the turbine floor. "Like a tiny earthquake!" said George, and then the noises sounded steady again.

"Right!" said the chief designer quickly, the excitation was put back on, and without any more "WOOF"s the system pulled back into step with the National Grid without any trouble.

Roger breathed a great sigh of relief, and the design chief grinned at Roger. "There you are! I told you it would be OK," and Roger also grinned and started to examine the rows of recording paper now spewed out over the floor.

"Yes!" said Roger, "everything is behaving as predicted," and he tried to keep the surprise out of his voice. Tests now proceeded with increasing power output from the turbine and with growing confidence all round.

Roger found himself busy running up and down from the turbine floor up to the control room, as the station super and his chief engineers preferred to stay in this vantage point. From there they could see the total picture of the effect the tests were having on the other generators and on the total output from the power station into the National Grid. "Did you know..." the station super barked at him after the first test, "that when you did that pole slip, all the lights in Poole did a flicker?" he paused, then not waiting for an answer. "Did the generator behave OK?"

"Yes," said Roger "Our Design Chief says everything is fine and we are ready to go ahead and work our way up to a full load run."

"Hrmph!" muttered the super. "Carry on, but take each step carefully, and stop immediately if any of you suspect any trouble."

Roger could see that the super was more worried than he sounded, and Roger found himself repeating his own chief's words of re-assurance. The only staff who were not apparently worried at all, were the control room operators. They were actually handling the control buttons and enjoying the experiments. Usually their lives were very humdrum, and this was something quite different. Watching their large panel of instruments with some moving in and out of areas marked red for danger was a brand new experience.

Finally, the last test was ready with the generator now on full output, and all the testers could sense the power driving through the system. The noise was much the same but there was now an urgent vibration under their feet that George assured Roger was quite normal. By now, there was an absolute mountain of paper recordings of results, and Roger and George were doing their best to keep them in some sort of order with added pencil notes saying which test was which. "It's going to take a wretched month to sort this lot out when we get back," moaned George, and they set all recorders going for the final big test.

By now, there was considerable confidence among all testers and even the station super was smiling. As predicted, even at full load, the system behaved just the same, and with the extra confidence of practice, the control room operators allowed the system to slip three poles before pulling back into synchronism. Thus on the turbine floor there were three large "WOOFs" as the poles were slipped, now much noisier than previously because of the heavy load, but with a perfect restoration afterwards. That signalled the end of the tests with a general feeling of satisfaction all round. It was now past the normal closing time for the day shift, and in no time at all, the station super and his retinue had gone home, leaving George and Roger and two juniors to do the tidying up. "Tell me the old, old, story," sighed George.

They were collecting the last pen recordings when suddenly George started to swear. "Can you bloody well believe it, just look at this!" and he held up one of the key recordings "I can't believe it!" he shouted, "look at it!" Roger looked. It was one of the most important records showing the heavy over-current inside the generator during the "WOOF" pole slips on full load, but just as the trace started, the recorder had run out of ink!

Roger and George looked at each other in total dismay. "This is the most important record," said Roger, "The tests are wasted! What can we do?"

"We'll do the damn run again," said George.

"But we can't," said Roger, "everyone in authority has gone home."

"So much the better!" grinned George. "Watch this." George picked up the intercomm and called up the Control Room. "We've got a problem," he said casually. "That last test you've just done. Some of the vital recordings have failed. Would you mind running it again? We can be ready in five minutes." A cheerful voice came back, "Sure, no problem, we're old hands at this now." and sure enough, the major full load run was repeated in no time. This time the records were perfect, George thanked the control staff and Roger, and they gathered up all the completed precious records and were ready to go home.

Suddenly, there was a screeching of brakes outside, it was the station super, and he came almost running into the control room where all the testers had just assembled before leaving.

"What's happened?" he said. "What's happened? Has there been an accident?" "No, no, not at all!" smiled George happily, speaking up as spokesman. "We just had to repeat the last run, the records weren't complete."

"I know!" spluttered the super. "I saw it! You slipped three more poles! I had just sat down to watch television, when my picture suddenly shrunk to half size, then recovered and did it three times! I thought we had lost the station!" He was so relieved to realise that everything was completely back to normal that he relaxed and even forgot to question who had given the authority.

The journey back to Witton was uneventful and Roger spent the next week in the Design Office helping to sort out all the recordings and make sure they were all properly labelled and could be compared with calculated predictions. George, as soon as they were back at base, was smartly called off to another job, much to his satisfaction. "I'm delighted to leave all the paperwork to you" he said to Roger with a great grin, "I can't stand hanging about here tidying up bumf, I'm off!" and he was away to another part of the country.

Roger wad hardly finished sorting out the records, when he was called into Switchgear Division and asked to go down to South Wales to join a team installing a new colliery winder system. The Skipper, of "nutcracker suite" fame was involved and he gave Roger an initial briefing. "This is an existing colliery," he said, "where they have been producing coal for twenty years, including all through the war, and using a steam winding engine. We are replacing this with an electric winder system that I am quite sure they will look at with very great suspicion. Also, we are introducing a new winder motor control system, that even the management themselves will worry about. This new system is much cheaper than the more established systems, and if it is successful, will bring us in a lot of good business, so we are all very anxious to make a good job of it." He paused. "I'm telling you all this so you are prepared for the likely reaction from some of the colliery workers. Especially watch out for the underground manager, the colliery has a good safety record, and the lives of all the men underground are his responsibility. Have you ever been down a coal mine?" he suddenly asked.

"No, I've never even been near one," admitted Roger.

"Well, I hope you enjoy yourself" Skipper grinned "Who do you think will be the first volunteers to ride down in the new winder?"

"I don't know," stammered Roger.

"You soon will, it'll be our Erection team of course, including you!" he laughed. "These miners are very suspicious, they can trust steam, hear it, smell it, hear the hooter, and know when all is well. Electricity is nasty silent stuff, so you will all have a real confidence building job on your hands."

The colliery was near the top of a lovely Welsh valley stretching away from Swansea, Roger was taken down to the site by a switchgear engineer called down to bring some extra fittings, and he had chosen a picturesque route over the head of the valley through the Black Mountains. It was a beautiful run, and Roger was entranced by the marvellous scenery all the way down. "This is the life!" he said to himself. "No wonder everyone wants to come on Outside Erection." The engineer chatted to him all the way down, he was as pleased as Roger to have a day off as he saw it and they took their time.

"You won't have much to do for a few days," the engineer said. "They haven't closed down yet for the Summer Holidays. When they do it will a mad rush to get the old steam winder stripped out and the electric one installed. They won't want to lose much production of precious coal, so it will be all hell let loose to get the new winder installed and tested within the two weeks."

"Is it always a rush like this?" asked Roger.

"Sure is," came the reply. "I've never known it any different."

"I've got a problem on my mind," said Roger as they drove along at a comfortable pace.

"Go on," prompted the engineer.

"Well when I was down at Poole, I was told the story of the senior designer who was sent out to South Africa to supervise a winder motor repair."

"You mean poor old Alec?" laughed the driver "everyone thought he was a lucky sod, but he spent all his time underground, and never saw a bloody thing. He is still moaning about it now!"

"But why was he underground?" asked Roger. "Surely the winding motor is up at the top on the surface?" "No, not on those very deep South African mines," explained his driver. "They have to have two stages, with a second winding engine down at half way."

"But why not a bigger winding motor at the top and use longer cables?"

"Aha!" chuckled his mentor "that's where you're quite wrong! Can't you guess?"

"No" confessed Roger, "that's why I ask."

"Well, the very simple reason is that you can't make the cables any longer."

"Why so?" persisted Roger.

"Because there is a natural maximum length to a cable that you can't exceed, if you try to go longer it will snap under its own weight. If you put in a bigger, stronger cable, the weight goes up exactly in proportion, so the snapping length is just the same." Roger thought for a minute "You mean that a long thin cable will snap at the same length as a big strong fat one?" asked Roger.

"You've got it in one" smiled the driver.

On approaching the colliery, Roger could hear the puffing of the steam engine and couldn't help noticing the large head sheaf wheels spinning away above. Suddenly the wheels slowed to a stop, paused, and soon started spinning away in the other direction with  considerable snorting and escaping steam noises from the engine house. "It looks like the end of the shift," said his driver as they came to a halt. Roger's eyes were on the pit head, he could see the long thick black greasy ropes moving through the top of the pit shaft, one going up and one going down, and as he watched a large black cage rose from the depths and carefully came to a stop with a great noise of hissing steam and mechanical screeching from two enormous wooden brakes as they closed on each side of a great wheel on the side of the winding drum. Out of the cage poured a group of miners, shaking their heads in the sunlight and streaming off to a building to return their helmets with the lamp at the front, some exchanged a few cheery words with the engine driver who sat on his seat watching them and smiling as they streamed past him. As Roger watched, a bell rang two sharp rings, the steam engine burst into life, and as suddenly as it had appeared, the cage dropped away down the hole again and Roger was left staring at the hissing ropes as they gathered speed.

"My goodness," he thought "this will be a big job, and no mistake!"

The erection engineer in charge of the changeover was a mechanical engineer from the company's parent works in the south of England. He was a gruff, weather-beaten man in his late forties "Not a man to argue with!" thought Roger as he was introduced. He sized Roger up and down, and said kindly, "Ever been on a colliery job before?"

"No", said Roger " I've never been near one before." He then added as an after-thought, "In fact, this is also my first visit to Wales."

"It's a lovely country," nodded the chief, "you'll get to love it in time. Now, we've fixed you up in digs here in the village with an old retired miner, and I expect he will tell you a tale or two. Someone will take you over there this evening."

"How long will I be here?" asked Roger as he really had no idea what the plans were.

"Well, it all depends how we get on. You are the only electrical boffin down here so once we've got the heavy stuff done it will be over to you." Roger looked startled, but before he could get a word out the chief could see the expression on Roger's face and laughed. "No no, don't panic, there will be several Switchgear engineers from Witton to get it all started, probably including Skipper, and you will learn all about it from them. But once it is running, and they are reasonably happy, they will leave you here for a week or so to give the colliery confidence. It is our general plan, and it usually works very well."

"I see," said Roger, realising that he was being dropped in the deep end once again "Ah well!" he ruminated, "I've had it done to me before, and it worked out OK, so let's hope for the best."

"I'll introduce you to the colliery electrician," continued the chief. "He is a real canny Welshman, and you will be working closely with him while you are here. We all call him Taffy, it's not his real name, but his proper welsh name is too much of a mouthful for us, but he doesn't mind." Roger nodded, and was taken across to a little office where Taffy was pouring over a set of drawings from Witton.

Taffy jumped to his feet, "I'm very pleased to meet you," he said in his lovely warm rolling Welsh accent and shook Rogers' hand warmly, "Come and sit down by me boy, and help me get my head round all these drawings I've been sent. Look at them!" There was a great pile all neatly tied in bundles, and Taffy waved them in the air with despair.

Roger found he could help Taffy straight away as he knew enough about the drawings to get him started. "This lot," he said pulling out the majority, "are only the control cubicle circuitry, and we can forget them to start with. *These* are the ones you need now," and he pulled out one or two that described the high voltage wiring for the motor, and the various inter-cubicle windings needed on site.

"Good, that's a lot better," said Taffy breathing a sigh of relief, "I can get the boys started on these, we have some electricity fitters from the Electricity Board to help us with the high voltage, and they can get started as well."

"Where is all the new equipment?" asked Roger, as he had seen no sign of anything so far.

"Oh, it's all still down in Swansea," explained Taffy "It's no good having it on site yet, we haven't got the room d'you see."

Roger could see very well. There wasn't an inch of space on the site that wasn't full of something; pieces of mining equipment, small gauge railway lines — some running to the slag heaps — spare coal trucks everywhere, odd wooden huts dotted around, and a general sprinkling of coaldust, dampness, and the unmistakeable smell of coal everywhere.

"Now you are here," said Taffy, getting up from his chair, "the first important task we have to do is to go and see the underground manager. He is the most important man on the site. All the miners trust him, and he wants to learn all about this new electric winding engine. He is very suspicious, and if he isn't happy, we won't get anyone to go down the pit. Come on, we'll go and make his acquaintance now." Taffy led the way to a small hut where they saw two men in earnest conversation together. The elder, the underground manager looked up with relief.

"You've come just at the right time Taffy," he boomed in a loud voice. "This is Gwilliam Evans, our trade union representative, and he is telling me that the miners are very worried about us taking out the steam winder and replacing it with the electric. They trust their lives to our steam winder with Garry and Thomas, our two drivers, and no one knows what is going to happen now."

"Don't you worry at all," said Taffy, speaking slowly in a soft, calming voice. "Electric winders are going in all over the valleys, and everyone is saying that they are safer and they give a better ride." He paused, and pushed Roger forward, "I know you are all worried, so was I once, and I have brought this young man from the factory to answer your questions. He has been to the university and he is an expert," he added with emphasis.

Roger swallowed hard and sat down on a rickety old chair proffered. "Been to University!" he thought. He knew plenty who had been there who he wouldn't trust to boil an egg.

"Now," said the underground manager opening the conversation, "I have heard that this new electric winding engine is to be supplied at three *thousand volts*," he repeated the three thousand with heavy emphasis. "Is that right?"

"Yes" said Roger nodding "that's the normal supply voltage for a large motor."

"But that could kill you" interrupted the representative, Gwilliam.

"Quite right," interrupted Taffy quickly, "but so could the electrics in your house, and they are only two hundred and forty volts."

"But *three thousand volts* is very different," said Gwilliam heavily, and the manager nodded in agreement.

Roger realised that these men were very serious, and the last thing he dare do was to treat their worries lightly. "In the industry," he explained, "*three thousand volts* is quite small. We are building equipment in the factory for *one hundred and thirty two thousand* volts as industry standard, and in the laboratories, we are experimenting at two *hundred and seventy five thousand.*"

Taffy chipped in, "The electric wires on the poles coming up through the valley are *eleven thousand* volts, and no one worries about those." "But that's not inside our winding engine" said the manager ponderously. "Inside our engine shed is too close."

Gwilliam nodded eagerly in agreement. "Say it gets out?"

"No," said Roger very carefully, "inside the motor, the windings supplied with the high voltage are very carefully wrapped in a tough waxed tape that can stop any voltage escaping. It is called insulation, and at all stages of the motor build, this insulation is constantly checked, When the motor is finished, the first thing the inspectors do is re-check the insulation, and even the merest hint of a leak and the machine is rejected, and the men responsible have to rebuild. If they make a mess of it more than once, they get the sack."

"But if it *did* escape," pursued Gwilliam "I have heard it can run down the cable and electrocute the men in the cage!"

"Absolutely impossible" said Roger, "the cables are on the big drum and they go up over the headsheaves, and all that metal is solidly connected to the earth. Any attempt would cause the electric supply to trip out at once."

"Before it even got out," interrupted Taffy, "just like a fuse blowing in your house."

"That maybe all right," said the manager slowly. "We shall have to think it over, but we shall want you clever people to take the first ride down the pit to prove it!"

"Of course they will," said Taffy. "It's part of the acceptance tests in the contract."

Later, Roger stood by the door of the engine shed and watched the rest of the miner's shift being brought to the surface. He was struck by the skill of the driver, who seemed to know just how much a little puff of steam could nudge the giant pistons and move the large brake drum just that extra inch or two to manage an exact positioning of the cage when it docked. There was a large chalk mark on the side of the great brake wheel, and an arrow on a fixed pillar, and the aim was to bring the giant wheel to a stop with the chalk mark exactly opposite the arrow. The driver seemed to be able to do this almost in an uncanny fashion without hesitation time after time. Taffy came across and joined him "That's Thomas, our senior driver on duty now," he volunteered. "He's a very good driver, and most of the time the miners are pleased with him."

"Why not all the time?" asked Roger.

"Well, it's not easy to always get the winder to behave just right, and sometimes he might take two or three shots to get the mark on the drum in just the right position. Until the cage is just in the right position, the surface manager can't clamp the cage and let the men out. Then the miners in the cage start shouting very rude remarks, they want to get out and get home."

Roger laughed, "But it's not his fault?"

"It's always the driver's fault," smiled Taffy. "You ought to see the trouble when we have to call in an outside driver sometimes. Until he gets used to the engine, a strange driver may take the best part of an extra hour to get everyone on the shift up to the surface, then there is blue murder in the air!"

Roger was silent, realising for the first time the close link that existed between these men and their machinery. "Perhaps we shouldn't take lifts so much for granted at home," he thought.

Roger carried on watching. "Taffy!" he suddenly asked, "that chalk mark on the drum is very important, why isn't it painted on properly? That bit of a chalk mark can't last very long?"

"It doesn't have to!" explained Taffy "we redo them every week."

"Why?" sounded Roger in surprise.

"Because little changes are happening to the ropes all the time, they slowly get older and stretch a bit, and we find a difference between cold days and hot days. The ropes are a sort of living thing to us. We have to understand them!"

Roger interrupted "There's also those yellow marks in a different position, what are those for?" he asked.

"That's when we're lifting coal" came the reply, "The ropes get stretched more with the heavier weight, so we need to pull the cage up about an extra couple of feet."

Roger nodded, "I suppose that's where the old saying come from about 'learning the ropes'," he mused to himself. "Even the simplest looking job is complex when you really understand it!"

"There's nothing you can do today," said Taffy, "so I'll take you across to your digs, you'll be with Mr and Mrs Neal Williams, he retired from this colliery two years ago and you will be very comfortable with him. He's been a miner all his life, and can tell you lots of tales if you ask him!"

"Fine," said Roger, "it's all very new to me." They walked down the road out of the colliery to the Williams' house, it was only about two hundred yards down the road and was one in a row of standard miners' terraced houses. Roger walked in, and was immediately made to feel very welcome and shown to the second bedroom upstairs which was spotless.

"This is my son's bedroom," explained Mrs Williams proudly with a rich welsh accent. "He is not here anymore. He has won a scholarship and has joined the Admirality." Roger let the mispronunciation of "Admiralty" go by, he felt too shy to comment. However, over the next two weeks he heard both the Williams proudly talk about their son in the "Admirality" at least once a day, and got quite used to their pronunciation with its lovely welsh lilt.

"You must call me Neal," said his host. "We always use Christian names down here in the valleys." He paused, "Have you ever been down a coal mine?"

"No, but I'm looking forward to it," smiled Roger.

"Ah well, they're very dirty places," Neal replied, "and you will have to watch your head! Most of us miners are short, but you must be a good six foot! are you not?"

"Just over," grinned Roger.

"Well you will have to keep your helmet on and keep bending low. When I started," he reminisced, "we didn't have helmets, the company couldn't afford them and nor could we. We were always getting somebody splitting his head open!"

Supper was a generous meal of lamb casserole with plenty of vegetables. Roger was hungry and ate with relish. As his plate started emptying, Mrs Williams leaned across. "I do like to see a body with a good appetite," she beamed. "Have some more," and before Roger could reply, another substantial heap was piled on to his plate.

"Steady on," he called in alarm, but his good hostess was in her element.

"My husband doesn't eat properly now he has retired," she explained. "It's nice to see my food being appreciated!"

Neal beamed at them from the other side of the table. "That's right," he said, "working down the pit makes you very hungry, but I don't need all that food now. If I'm not careful, I shall grow into fat!"

Mrs Williams snorted, "Fat! I keep telling him, he's too thin, he can't even keep a body warm at night!" She looked at her husband and they both burst into laughter. As they finished eating, a steaming large brown teapot was produced. Mrs Williams retired to the scullery, and Roger and his host were left on their own.

There was an old Bakelite cased wireless set on the windowsill, and Neal switched it on, apologising at the same time for the poor reception. "I'm sorry about this," he said, "but it has always been like this. They say you understand the electricity?" he asked hopefully, looking at Roger.

"Not that sort," said Roger hastily, "I'm a power systems man, wireless sets are electronics which we don't study at all."

Neal looked crestfallen." They told me at the colliery that you would know how to mend it," he said, sounding disappointed.

Roger laughed apologetically "the only thing I know about valve wireless sets is that they have to be well earthed."

Neal interrupted him eagerly. "I know that! I've made a special connection to a copper pipe underneath the stairs. Will you have a look at it?"

Roger agreed, although he knew he couldn't help him at all. Several times at home, neighbours had asked him to have a look at their wireless sets, and he had come to hate the subject like the plague. Neal opened a tiny door under the stairs, and there was the end of a bare earth wire from the wireless set wrapped meticulously round a foot long piece of shiny copper pipe. The only snag was that the pipe itself was not connected to anything, but sat there isolated on a neat pile of dry newspapers! Roger smiled broadly, "But that's not an earth at all!" he said, but Neal was indignant.

"It is!" he replied, "the shop in Swansea where I bought it," he went on slowly, "said to connect the socket marked 'earth' on the back of the wireless on to a piece of the water pipe system, and that's what I've done!"

"Well, not quite like this," explained Roger gently, and proceeded to explain exactly what had to be done. "Thank you very much," said Neal happily. "There you are! I knew you would know all about it."

Roger hastily changed the subject. "I was watching the steam winder this afternoon, it was very interesting, I can see it's a very skilled job."

"Ah," nodded Neal. "Thomas was on today, he's our best driver. We all trust him, but," he added, "he is a very superstitious man and he's always on to the engineers about something not being quite right. Our chief mechanic says that Thomas is sometimes a real 'pain in the bottom,' if you will pardon my language," he said apologetically.

"Sure," said Roger laughing. "But what causes the *pain?*"

"Well, for one thing, every now and again, on a Monday morning, Thomas will summon up the chief mechanic and complain that the brakes are stiff, and the winder isn't safe." He paused to roll a cigarette. "Now the chief knows that there's nothing wrong, but he sorts out Thomas by coming up with a large oil can in his hand. 'Right-ho Thomas,' he shouts. 'Try this,' and he squirts a stream of oil into a hole near the base of the big brake block hinges. 'Try that!' he shouts."

"What does the oil do?" asked Roger.

"Nothing at all!" laughed Neal, "it's just a hole in the base, and the oil runs away to waste at the bottom of the drum pit. But Thomas doesn't know this, and he will work the brakes once or twice and either announce he's satisfied, or sometimes ask for a drop more oil."

Roger laughed. "Doesn't Thomas ever suspect something?"

"No never," said Neal leaning back. "It's gone on like that for years. Mind you," he added, leaning over and looking closely at Roger, "we did have a real problem with the brakes some years ago where in the end Thomas was proved right."

"Go on!" said Roger getting very interested.

"One winter," said Neal leaning back comfortably in his chair, "Thomas kept complaining that the brakes were acting particularly stiff first thing in the Monday morning when he came on shift, and that the oiling routine wasn't quite sorting it out. He kept saying that this only happened when there was a bitter cold wind coming down the valley from the north-east. We all laughed and told him it was his lumbago playing up, but he wasn't amused and used to take the first half dozen groups of miners down the shaft with an extra caution that used to get some of the miners quite angry."

"How strange!" said Roger. "Did he go and see a doctor?"

"Not him!" laughed Neal. "But he kept on persisting you see, and so we went over the whole winder with a tooth comb, but there was absolutely nothing wrong. The mechanics keep everything in the winder house absolutely spotless all the time."

"I noticed that." agreed Roger "every piece of the machinery looked absolutely spotless and shining like exhibits in a museum."

"That's right," continued Neal. "Now when the spring came, Thomas's problem, as we called it, disappeared and we forgot all about it, except for Thomas of course, but we were used to a few grumbles from him you see, so no one took any more notice."

"But what's the north east wind got to do with it?" asked Roger.

"Ah well," continued Neal. "That's where we were all wrong!"

"How on earth..." began Roger but Neal carried on.

"We have a regular building inspection in the spring when the weather is better, and, what do you think they found?"

"Go on," said Roger.

"They reported damaged brickwork on the north-east corner of the winder house, and when we checked, there was a small crack through the bricks right behind the main steam pipe feeding the brakes! You couldn't see it from the inside, but what was happening was that a cold North Easter could get through and probably cause some steam condensation inside the pipe, and then the brakes would play up until the water drained out the system!"

"Good Lord!" exclaimed Roger "so Thomas was right all the time?"

"We think so," said Neal cautiously "that's the theory anyhow. We patched up the brickwork, and there was no problem next winter, so we suppose Thomas was indeed right."

The next day, delivery started on the equipment needed for the new winder. The first consignment was only smaller items including the control panels where Taffy could find space for.

"Where's this new electric winder motor then?" a group of miners asked.

"Not yet Boyohs," answered Taffy, "that will come last, when the new winder house is ready. We've got to clear your old engine out and set the new concrete foundations before we bring in the electric engine."

"Will it be strong enough Taffy?" was the next question.

"Of course it will!" laughed Taffy. "Now don't you worry about it. I tell you now, once the new winder is in and running smoothly you will be very pleased with it! Now, just you get on with your work and let me get on with mine!" The miners laughed a little uncertainly and then walked off. Taffy turned to Roger. "I'm getting this all the time," he grinned. "We had better get it right between us when the time comes."

The Site Erection Manager came over. "I'm working out the time-table for the change-over," he said brusquely. "The problem will be fitting it all in. The best we can do is to get all the civil and mechanical work done by about Thursday of the second week. If you electrics can get the motor installed by then, we shall be able to do some basic runs on Friday to check out all the couplings and give the drum a few turns. If that looks good, you can have the system Friday night to check out all the new-fangled speed control system, and then on Saturday we can carry out some slow speed automatic winding cycles on the man winding cam controller. If that's OK, we'll follow up with the faster runs on the coal winding cycle. You will also have to squeeze in the training of the drivers on the Saturday, and then on Sunday morning we will have the formal runs and acceptance tests. The first shift of miners is due to go down Sunday evening." He looked up from his papers. "What do you think of that, can you manage do you think?"

Roger swallowed hard, he was used to several weeks when in the laboratory for checking out new control systems. One Friday night only! This was impossible!

Taffy spoke up. "We will do our best," he said slowly, "but you're not giving us much time for the electrics are you!" "Good on you Taffy," said the Manager and strode off before there was time for another word.

"Taffy!" exploded Roger "how on earth can we do all our stuff on just the one Friday night! We really need at least two or three days.

"No chance Roger," said Taffy lugubriously shaking his head "we electrics are always the tail-end-charlies, and expected to work miracles."

The next two weeks seem to fly by, with Roger marvelling at the ingenuity of the miner's team. He was especially impressed when the large winding motor was unloaded from a large road transporter. It had to somehow be carried across the narrow busy yard to the new winding house, and there was no way the large transporter could get anywhere near. Roger watched with his heart in his mouth as the motor was lifted off and precariously perched on a little coal carrier that travelled on the narrow gauge railway lines running all over the yard. It was then very carefully inched across the yard, over the coal lumps and the puddles, with men holding guide ropes each side to steady the balance, and two surface pit ponies slowly tugging the load along. Everything somehow survived, the motor was duly installed, and the day to start the electric tests loomed steadily nearer. Skipper Emms and a small team arrived at the start of the second week, and Roger breathed with relief. Skipper knew the Site Erection Manager of old, and with various give and take arrangements between the two of them, the team were surprisingly just about on time by the second Saturday morning.

During the electrical tests, Roger had one scare and a lesson on not panicking that he never forgot. During the Friday night, as they were testing, someone smelt burning from one of the control cubicles. The cubicle was down in a basement underneath the winder floor and Roger was sent down to investigate. He opened the cubicle door, and could see immediately the source of the smell. One of the control resistances, fitted at the last moment in the factory, was getting very heated. Roger could see the new paint on the surface starting to blister a little with the current going through it. Roger peered closely at this for a second or two and decided that an emergency call was needed. He was a long way away from the team up above and without looking up, he shouted at the top of his voice, "Resistances number thirty-two is burning!"

A very quiet voice, right at his elbow said, "Thank you," and looking up in astonishment, he found Skipper right beside him. He had followed Roger down, "Thank you my boy," said Skipper quietly again, looking over Roger's shoulder at the resistor. "That's how they work." Roger had never felt so small in his life. But Skipper just grinned and they both went back upstairs.

A little incident that occurred the day after Skipper arrived impressed itself deeply in Roger's mind. The electrical team couldn't do much work that day, and Taffy was explaining to Skipper about Roger's digs and mentioned Roger's host Mister Williams. "Do you know," he said, "old Neal Williams worked in this colliery all his life, and we don't think he's ever been further afield than just outside the village. He told me once that he has never even had a ride in a motor car!" Skipper Emms didn't comment, but that afternoon it was a glorious sunny day; he went and found Neal and took him up in his car for a two hour drive up the valley and over the top of the Black Mountains.

It was the talk of the colliery next day, and Williams himself walked around in a second heaven. "It was like a great birrrd!" he kept telling everyone with his welsh lilt. "Just like a great birrrd".

Testing and acceptance progressed smoothly, and Roger found himself, with the rest of the engineers, being assembled for the first trial run with men on board. By then, there had been a number of unmanned runs, and Roger felt both semi-confident and apprehensive at the same time. They all had to put on miner's helmets and overalls, and amid much banter they gathered at the pit head ready to start. Roger stared at the cage. It suddenly looked much smaller and fragile now they were close up to it, and when he stared up at the big wheels of the head sheaves above, his only thought was that the long thin cable stretching up above them and over the wheel down to the engine shed would be the only thing between them and crashing down the black hole to their doom! No one else seemed bothered in the slightest! They had all done this before. With his heart in his mouth, Roger tried to grin as the cage door shut with a clang and the shrill bell sounded with the standard signal, "Descend with men on board."

The clamps were withdrawn, and after the slightest of jerks, the cage started to glide down easily and steadily. Taffy was with them and he was the first to speak. "Well boyoh," he said to Roger "All aboard the skylark! How do you like it?"

"It's fine," stammered Roger, but could not take his eyes off the sides of the pit gliding up past them. They were lit every few yards by small sunken pilot lights. The walls, were black, dirty, wet and dripping, and seemed surprisingly close on the one side. What impressed Roger most was the total eerie silence; no noise from the winding engine came down the pit shaft, and he felt he was entering into a new world. He watched the black oily rope of the other cage flying up silently past them. Down and down they went, and suddenly, like a big silent ghost, the other cage loomed into view for a second and then disappeared above them just as silently on its way up. The total silence of the other cage as it appeared, slipped past, and silently disappeared again only added to Roger's sense of unreality.

Taffy interrupted Roger's thoughts. "The main thing we must study," he said, "is to see just how smoothly we land at the bottom. If that's not smooth, then we shall have to adjust the cam profile."

One of the engineers spoke. "The trouble is that the miners want it both ways, they want to get to work as fast as possible, but they want to stop without the slightest jerk!"

"Thomas was very good at that," said another, and they all agreed.

Suddenly Roger felt the cage slowing down, and now for the first time he became aware they were hanging on the end of a long rope. As the cage slowed, so it see-sawed up and down a little like a weight on the end of a piece of elastic, Roger felt slightly queasy and held on to the rail "Is everything OK?" he whispered to Taffy, but Taffy only grinned back.

"Of course it is, we can't stop the rope stretching you know!" and Roger bit his lip as they suddenly emerged into a bright lamplit area and the cage very slowly, indeed, very slowly came to a halt at the pit bottom.

"Not bad for a beginning," grunted an engineer looking at his watch. "We shall be able to prune a few seconds off that," and they all stepped out of the cage to have a quick look round before being called back for the return journey.

The rest of the day was uneventful; various inspections were made, Skipper was very much in demand, and by evening the preliminary engineers had gone down the pit, and eventually they were followed by the first shift of miners. "That's another job done!" said Skipper with satisfaction and turned to Roger. "Well lad, we shall be leaving you here now on your own for a week. Will you be OK?"

Roger swallowed hard, "I hope so, but what if anything goes wrong?"

"It's unlikely" said Skipper reassuringly "but if it does, it's most likely to be a mechanical problem and you can't help. If it is something where you can help, have a go, but don't hesitate to call me up if you're stuck. Mining engineers are the most resourceful in the world, and I've never known them yet not sort a problem out." Skipper turned to the assembled erection team, "I know what you're waiting for!" he said with a chuckle, let's go down to Swansea and have a cup of tea or something," and they all grinned.

Seated comfortably in a public house later, one of the engineers turned to Skipper. "Your comment about mining engineers," he said. "We had an example of their resourcefulness last year down in Kent, at a colliery in Chislett, near Canterbury. We were introduced to the chief mechanical engineer when we arrived, he was a bit of a character, and had pepped up his pre-war Ford Prefect car with a much larger V8 engine.

"Impossible!" said someone.

"Not for him," the speaker continued, "he had it in their colliery workshop for a month cussing and swearing away, making special brackets and had bits and pieces fitted until he succeeded."

"Did it work?" they asked.

"Yes and no!" came the reply, "it would go fine, but he had trouble with the steering."

"That all?" came a sarcastic comment, and the storyteller grinned and carried on. "He found the trouble was that the extra weight was distorting the chassis and hence the front wheel alignments"

"Silly bugger," said a listener.

"Aha, but he got over that as well. You won't believe this, but he hacked the car around and fitted two rolled steel joists inside right through from back to front that evenly distributed all the weight."

"Give him a bike!" said a voice.

"Not for him," continued our story teller. "He was proud of his super-duper car and drove around in it for several months showing off his handiwork. But another real snag emerged. The brakes weren't up to the strain of the heavier weight, and he had a few nasty accidents. In each case his car came out OK but the other vehicles were really knocked to buggery."

There were hoots of laughter. "What happened then?"

"He was really upset because the police became involved and he was refused any more insurance. So after all that, he had to scrap it."

The engineer re-filled his tankard "The main story to tell you though is about a bad accident we had with the winder."

Everyone pricked up their ears "What happened?"

"We had handed over the new winder and everything went well for a few days, when one of the drivers became over-confident and drove a load of coal up much too fast into the pit top. The cage crashed through the stops and run up into the head sheaves where it was arrested but not before it had snapped one of the guide ropes, and the bottom cage came crashing down at the pit bottom with a great bang and a pile of dust, and then there was this rumble of the guide rope coming coiling down, damaging the pit sides on the way, and piling up on top of the crashed bottom cage.

"Anybody hurt?"

"No thank goodness! The miners at the shaft bottom sensed the cage was coming too fast, and had scattered like lightning just before the cage and the rope came tumbling down."

"Wow! What happened then?" "That's my point" said the story teller. The mechanical engineers took over, cleared up the guide rope remains, got the men out in no time and had refitted all the ropes, repaired the shaft sides, and they were back in production within two days."

"They couldn't have helped poor old Jock down here the other week!" said Taffy, who was with them, and many of them started to laugh.

"What happened?" asked Skipper.

"Haven't you heard?" said an engineer. "He's our resident maintenance engineer down here in Swansea. He lost his car last week, but all the rest of us can do is only laugh about it!"

" What's funny about that?" queried Skipper with a quizzical lift of his eyebrows.

"I'll tell you," said Taffy. "He 'phoned us up and I went to fetch him, he was in a terrible temper, he was fond of his car, and being a Scotsman his language was awful, I could hardly understand him".

"Go on" said Skipper grinning.

"Well, he had gone over the top to the next valley to repair a damaged overhead pole, and parked his car at the side of the road to get into the field. Unfortunately," and he spoke with a laugh in his voice, "Jock had parked underneath a tall bank with a field of cows in the field above. He was working away, when he heard a peculiar noise and a crash, and went back to find a cow had broken through the barbed wire, fallen down and landed smack on top of his car!" Those of the group who had not heard the tale before burst into astonished laughter.

"You see!" said Taffy, "everyone laughs about it."

"I don't expect the cow did" grinned Skipper, "what was the damage?"

"They've declared the car a right-off and the cow had to be put down."

Another engineer joined in "The worst part of it is, the insurance people have now rejected any claim from Jock as they have declared it an 'Act of God!'."

"The bastards," said Skipper, and they all supped their beer reflectively.

Another engineer joined in the conversation. "I hear that our boss, Ernie Jukes, has at last got a company car".

"That's about time!" said another, "he is always going out at all hours anywhere in the country wherever there is a call from a power station. The whole industry respects him as one of the best at sorting out any running problems on turbo-generators."

"How do you think he finally managed to get a company car?" asked the first speaker.

"I happen to know," interrupted Skipper "I got involved. Ernie had a call in the middle of the night from the super at Hams Hall power station, the super had been called in by the night shift because of vibrations and noise from number three turbine-generator set. As you know, that is a new, very big station, and is our pride and joy in the Midlands. It is the company's prestige site at the moment and although we have had our troubles, it is settling down nicely now."

The listeners waited expectantly, "So what happened?"

Skipper laughed. "It was an absolutely foul night, raining cats and dogs, and Ernie had only that day had a row with our managing director about his not having a company car, so he got dressed, got his old push-bike out, took his time, and cycled across to Ham Hall in the pouring rain. It took him a good hour to get there, while the station super and his senior staff had to stand around in the station worrying and biting their nails."

"Good for him!" said the listeners laughing, "only Ernie could get away with that."

"That's right," agreed Skipper. "The upshot was the super was furious when Ernie arrived dripping wet from head to toe and sloshed around the super's brand new shiny office. He then went and listened to the running set and assured them they had nothing to worry about."

Everybody laughed, they could all picture the scene, managers in a new power station were always very nervous in the early days. "The next day," continued Skipper, "our managing director had an extremely heated telephone phone call from the station super, and within a week, Ernie had a company car!"

Roger always thoroughly enjoyed these talks after work. "This is when you learn what engineering is really all about." he said to himself.

Skipper was in a relaxed mood, and he opened up on another story. "Did you all hear about our fun and games with that swing bridge near Gateshead?" he asked.

"Not all of us," said one, "but we'd love to hear it from you."

"It was another very prestige job," Skipper started. "It was a new swing bridge across a fairly wide stretch of water, and was going to be an important new crossing in the neighbourhood and would mean a lot to the local community. We had never tackled anything like this before, and we had a lot of trouble with the electric control system. Swing bridges are very heavy cumbersome things, and they take a lot of starting and a lot of stopping. Especially to do the manoeuvre of opening and closing as fast as possible, and yet always stop in absolutely the right place."

"That's no different to our winders," interjected Taffy. "We have to be spot-on as well."

"You are quite right," said Skipper, "but somehow, when standing in the open air with a howling wind cutting across the water, and often in the rain, it seemed to us a different order of problem, and it became a long and miserable job trying to get within the specification." The engineers all nodded in sympathy. "To cut a long story short," went on Skipper, "we finally got the system to be fairly consistent and prepared for the handover day. We had to meet a specification of three minutes to close the bridge and be within one inch at the docking point. We were still uncertain of being accurate every time, and yet the very next day we were committed to having the official tests. We really needed another week, but the local council chief engineer wouldn't hear of it."

Everyone waited expectantly while Skipper had a long slow drink. "Come the day," he resumed, "we were astonished to find that, with all the interest in the bridge, the day had been declared a sort of unofficial local public holiday and a large crowd were expected to attend. Now the problem was, that because we were not yet really confident of our control system, I had rehearsed with the engineers a manual system of docking that relied on me watching the bridge closely as it came into dock, and then giving a surreptitious signal to the control engineer when to manually slam on the final braking and come to a halt on the mark. Like you Taffy," said Skipper, "we had painted a large white mark, both on the road and the swinging bridge, and they had to line up as we stopped. We had practised this for an hour the day before and had got it down to a fine art." Now came the fun and games," said Skipper. "The first thing was the council staff came and roped off an area for their dignitaries, which of course covered the exact spot where I had practised standing for my braking signal. In fact, by the time they had sorted out their seating and chairs, there was hardly any room left for me anywhere!" Everyone listening was starting to grin "You can laugh!" said Skipper, "but we were in trouble, as the only place from where I could stand, was where the engineer working the brake wouldn't see me at all! We had a hurried discussion between the team, and I found a spot from where I could shout to him, and we decided that would have to do."

"When there's a will, there's a way." murmured a listener.

"Now the problem became even more complicated," Skipper carried on, "because with five minutes to go, and a crowd already assembling, of all things a ruddy brass band rolled up and commandeered the only area left! Before I had gathered my wits enough to sort out what to do, the band started up and you couldn't even hear yourself think, let alone shout out any signal."

"What on earth did you do?" was the immediate question.

"We got round it," laughed Skipper, "but it was one of my most 'heart in the mouth' moments. What we did was hastily arrange a relay of two signallers, I found a spot where I could just about see the mark, and as the bridge trundled into position, I somehow managed to pass on the signal at the right time with the band going at full blast, and everyone craning their necks to see the mark. In the end, their brand new bridge came to a stop in exactly the right position."

"Phew!" said the listeners, "I bet you felt relieved."

"Relieved!" laughed Skipper, "to use a phrase from Peter Armitage, I didn't know whether to shit myself or wind my watch."

The next day, Skipper and the Erection staff left, leaving Roger behind. "You'll be OK" said Skipper as they left. "There's just a slight problem still with the incoming circuit breaker, that's the big one you have to switch on to feed the 3 kv winder motor and the control cubicles. When you pull the lever down to close it, it sometimes springs out again on a spurious trip. I've phoned up the works to send down a fitter to adjust it, we can't seem to get it right."

"Fine" said Roger, trying to sound convinced. "I'll be ready for him." and he watched them go with a slight feeling of apprehension. The next day, the switchgear fitter arrived and looked at the unreliable breaker. After a while he took Roger aside.

"I've done the best I can," he said, "but this batch are giving a bit of trouble when they are new, but it will be fine when it has settled down. Until then what you might have to do is to be careful, open the cabinet, and put your foot on the toggle here," and he demonstrated to Roger just where to place it, "and hold it in for a few seconds until the switch is fully down, and then it will hold OK.

Roger had done his time in Switchgear works, so he understood. "That will be no problem," he smiled and considered the matter solved.

Three days later, very early in the morning, while Roger was still asleep, there came a loud knocking on the street door. It woke Roger, and he could hear Mrs Williams talking; it was Taffy. Roger jumped out of bed, he sensed trouble, and hastily looked out of the window to see if the head sheaves were spinning. It was still half dark, but Roger could see enough. The big wheels were quite still and stayed still! Roger knew what this meant, and he was already half dressed when Mrs Williams came up the stairs "It's Taffy" she said. "He wants you urgently, he can't get the winder to go."

"Coming" said Roger, hurrying down to see Taffy standing there waiting, "I'm sorry to call you so early," he said apologising, "but when I try to close the supply beaker, it just trips out on me!"

"Ah! I know the problem," said Roger feeling relieved, and they both hurried back to the colliery. Roger went straight to the main control cubicle, grabbed the breaker handle and pulled it down, holding the toggle switch in with his foot as he had been shown. There were peculiar noises that Roger couldn't place, but he held on with his foot a bit longer and suddenly every single light in the colliery went out and the noises stopped. There was an unearthly silence, Taffy came running up, "What have you done?" he asked in wonderment and at the same time a miner came running in shouting excitedly. "Taffy! Taffy! All the lights have gone out right down the vallee!" He repeated himself several times in a voice of wonder, "All down the Affon vallee! not a light anywhere!"

Roger and Taffy stood there looking at each other in utter bewilderment. "It must be something we've done," said Taffy staring at the cubicles, and Roger could only silently agree, but he had absolutely no idea what to do.

As they stood there at a loss, rescue came from below when a cleaner came up from below and casually said, "What's happened to the big dippers in the big water bath? We were told we always have to keep that water running?"

"That's right" exclaimed Roger and Taffy together, and Taffy continued angrily.

"Instructions are that *that* water supply must be never be turned off without permission from the winder house."

"Well, someone didn't know that. It's been turned off" said the cleaner.

Roger's mind was racing. "If that water supply fails the dippers run automatically to the short circuit position! That means that when we tried to close up we had a full 11 kv electrical short circuit through the motor on to the supply!"

"Ah, that explains everything" said Taffy sounding relieved; "No problem! I'll phone up our friends in the Supply Board Control Centre in Swansea and tell them what has happened. They will be very pleased to hear and will re-connect the valley supply in a jiffy."

Sure enough, power supply came back in no time, Taffy and Roger made sure the water controller was back with the cascade water running smoothly over the dippers, and Roger had a careful sniff of the motor. He had learned that trick in Standard Test and here there was no smell of over-heating. "Good!" He smiled to Taffy. "That over-current supply cut-out at Swansea saved our motor from damage. I think everything's OK now, shall we start again?"

"If you're happy," agreed Taffy, and this time everything worked perfectly and the big black wheels were soon spinning again. Roger went back for his breakfast "Every blessed light in the vallee" he mimicked to himself "they won't let me forget this one!"

The next week passed without incident, although Roger found himself getting out of bed as soon as it was light, and standing at the window waiting for the head sheaves to start spinning. If they were stationary, he stood there with his eyes glued on them, praying for them to start. Once they started again, he relaxed and looked forward to another trouble free day. One memorable day that week, Taffy took him down the pit and right up to a coal face. How Roger did enjoy the visit, he only banged his head about three times during the whole trip! Taffy was greatly amused "Serve you right for being so bloody tall!" he said.

Roger was called back to Witton after an uneventful further week, and his next assignment was to go and join a large group of mixed Outside Erection and Switchgear Control staff commissioning a new a very large new rolling mill at the Steel Company of Wales. Once again, this was a new development incorporating the latest slabbing and rolling techniques, starting with a massive slab of red- hot steel, and passing it though a succession of rollers on a moving conveyor belt system. As the slab was squeezed it became thinner and longer, and speeded up until at the last pass, the output strip would be flying out at sixty miles an hour where it would be automatically wound up into a large roll.

There had been many difficulties during the build, and when Roger arrived he was not surprised to find that the commissioning team included many senior engineers that he knew from his days in the laboratories and Rectifier Division. The team was in a state of near exhaustion, many long hours had been needed to sort out the thousand and one little snags that had occurred in such a complex operation. Many machines, linked control systems spread over nearly a quarter of a mile of a conveyor belt system, and the many vital safety features incorporated, meant that the job was one of the largest they had yet tackled. Some time for this trial testing had been allowed for this in the estimates, but this time had been greatly overrun by an unexpected problem that the team leader, one of Witton's best outside erection engineers, named Ken, described to Roger on his arrival. He recounted this story the first evening to a group of fresh site engineers when they were sitting around comfortably in a pub.

"The initial drive, as you know" Ken started off "is a large direct current speed controlled motor of three thousand horse power. We had completed its mounting and I was watching the mechanical boys busy connecting in the powerful gear chain drive to get down to the shaft

speeds needed for the initial powerful slabbing press. Out of curiosity, I just idly went through the gear chain in my head, keeping a mental note of the direction of rotation as we progressed through them. The motor started at clockwise, the next step is antclockwise of course, then clockwise again, and so on until I reached the main mill driveshaft going through the wall into the long conveyor belt shed next door. This was slow *clockwise*, and I thought nothing of this at the time. During the night I was chewing over the day's

events, and suddenly thought with a start, that surely the drive going into the wall, and directly coupled to the giant press needed to be *anti-clockwise?*"

He paused for a sip, "Naturally, I just laughed at myself, 'can't count' I thought, and went back to sleep. However, next day for amusement I retraced the gear train and again reached *clock-wise* going through the wall. My next step was to stroll down several hundred yards until I could turn the corner and get back to where I could check the mill on the other side of the wall. I was right! The drive needed to be *anti-clock!* Getting slightly rattled I saw the chief mechanical engineer standing there and said, 'This mill needs an anti-clock drive doesn't it'." He looked surprised at my assumed poor knowledge of the mechanics in front of us and just said, 'Of course.' 'Well,' I said, 'I make the drive coming through from the motor as *clock-wise*'. The chief just laughed. "Don't be so bloody silly, you just can't count, that's your trouble" So I left him and went back for a third check but still no joy." Ken paused again and took another sip. "It was like cross-checking some maths. You know there's a mistake, but you just can't see it."

He was interrupted by a listener "Were you right?" he asked.

"It turned out I was," said Ken, "but it took a lot of persuading the mechanicals, they were up to their eyes in work and didn't want to listen. Still in the end, after several more of us had checked it through, we all agreed it was wrong. The chief mechanical then said, "Well, your motor will just have to go the other way round, that's all! Just reconnect, and change the number-plate on the side."

"But surely that's a problem?" interrupted Roger. "I believe these large machines are designed to only run one way round, the secondary windings inside and the big commutators are built just for one direction of rotation!"

"Correct", said Ken. "I explained this to the chief mechanical engineer and it slowly sank in. Well then." he said, 'You've got a bleedin' problem haven't you! Nothing to do with me! Get on the 'phone and sort out your bloody Design Office!'"

One of the listeners interrupted. "But that's a major problem! I know these big DC motors. You *can* run in reverse of course, but after about half-load they start to spark across the commutator! There's a lot of re-design to do to the change the direction of rotation!"

"Precisely!" said Ken, "so I knew we had a very nasty problem. We were already up against time schedules, and I thought of the panic there would be back at the Works, and wondered how on earth I could tell them."

"What a job!" said another, "what did you do?"

Ken shrugged, "I simply had to 'phone up and tell them of course, but then I had exactly the same problem in getting the designers to believe me as I had down here! In fact the initial opinion was that I was off my rocker. They checked their design spec and confirmed they were right, the spec called for a clockwise rotation of the motor. 'Have less beer next time,' they said dismissively, and virtually hung up on me."

"Well, that wasn't much help!" said the listener in an angry tone.

"That was my reaction," agreed Ken, and I was just considering going back to Witton personally for a big row, when the phone rang again. It was the Chief Designer himself. 'Ken,' he said in a very subdued voice, 'we've just had all the civil drawings out and you are quite right! God knows how this had happened. What the hell are we going to do?'"

"I bet you really blew your top at them," said the same listener. "I would have given them blue murder!"

Ken laughed, "That wouldn't have helped, once everyone had calmed down we sorted out a plan. The necessary changed bits were rushed through, and two top winders came down and did the re-winding of the motor. However, it took about two months, and that's why we are running late."

However, by the time Roger joined them, the plant was running smoothly at last, and all Roger had to do was help in packing up the test equipment and getting it all sent back to Witton. He spent some time watching the mill in action and appreciated what a mammoth undertaking it had been. To see the initial red hot slabs passing through the rollers, all automatically, and then being squeezed by a succession of rollers with a tremendous clamour of noise and heat, Roger found awe-inspiring. When finally the still very hot, high speed strip came streaming out the end, and was automatically wound into great rolls he realised just how enormous the whole exercise had been. As he travelled back with the others, he felt a real warm feeling of self-confidence growing inside himself. "I'm becoming part of a great team," he thought. "There is nothing in this world that will ever beat us!"

A few days later, when Roger was back at the works, he heard the final twist to the story. A few days later, the Skipper was called to a top brass meeting with the managing director, Mr J. J. Gracie. When he arrived, he found Ken already in the Boardroom together with many senior engineers and the Chief Accountant. The MD came straight to the point, "Mr Emms!" he said, sounding very severe, "I have had the managing director of the Steel Company of Wales on the telephone this morning, and although he concedes that the plant is now working, he is far from satisfied. He pointed out that the delays had cost him several million pounds in lost production, and also that his staff were complaining that you have not left them any operating manuals!" He paused for effect. "And as a result the Managing Director is saying that he will not sanction the final payment to us for all our work until his engineers receive a full and adequate set of operating manuals." There was total silence in the room, all present knew that a lot of money was involved, and no one knew what to say. All the engineers present also knew that a full set of operating manuals was still a huge job to be done. The MD then continued "So what I want to know is, what you have to say about it Mr Emms, and what you are going to do about it!".

Skipper spoke for the first time "Yes Mister Gracie, we are aware that the manuals have still to be done, but we have had a few problems, and with a bit of luck we are now in the clear. Once we have got our breath back, we can get started on the manuals. However, I assure you they do have enough information to keep going for the moment."

The MD interrupted, "But what's this about these manuals? How long will they take?"

Skipper considered. "It is quite a big job, there are many details to be covered. As an estimate, we are looking at least nine to twelve senior man-months to cover everything."

The MD snorted and put his hands on the table for the big decision. "Very well then Mr Emms, I want you to put twelve men on the task, and have it done by the end of the month!"

There was an almost audible gasp around the room, most of them understood enough to know that this was absolutely impossible, there were only about three men in the world who knew the new system that intimately! They waited with baited breath to see what Skipper would say.

Skipper rose to the occasion. He just said quietly, "I'm sorry Mister Gracie, we'll do the best we can, but it's not quite like shovelling shit you know!"

Despite the serious tone of the meeting, Skipper's words broke the ice and there were grins all round. Even Mr Gracie had to smile. Plenty more was said but to little avail, and Skipper words became a byword for many a day.

CHAPTER 11

"Make Oi Larf"

The Apprentices Association at the factory had a long history. It had been formed many years ago, and now, in Roger's second year of apprenticeship, was celebrating its twenty-fifth anniversary. The association had become a part and parcel of the fabric of the site community, with many ex-"Apes" now in senior company positions including one member on the main board. Their nominal president was the current managing director of the whole group of companies, Sir Harry Railing who in the past he had spent time at the works, and he still kept a personal interest in apprentices' activities. However, no thoughts of such lofty ambitions were in the minds of Roger and a group of apprentices who were busy getting down to their latest, rather ambitious brain-wave.

At some of the Hall parties, Roger and like-minded friends had written funny sketches which had all been well received and they now fancied themselves as budding actors, so when a manager jokingly said they ought to be on the stage, their immediate reaction was, "Why not?" This idea had festered until in the end, they found themselves entering into the company's annual drama festival at the Fortune Theatre in London. A producer from the works operatic society then volunteered to organise the venture, and they were now getting down to the serious business of learning their lines.

Their producer Peter was an ex-"Ape" himself who now worked in one of the drawing offices. He had the reputation of having considerable literary merit, and was a prominent member of the work's amateur dramatic society. For this occasion, he extracted all the comic rustic scenes from Shakespeare's *A Midsummer-Night's Dream* and turned them into a one act play. After a few rehearsals, Roger had confessed to Peter that he had found Shakespeare very boring at school, but now he was thoroughly enjoying the magic of the words, as indeed were the rest of the motley apprentice cast.

This particular evening, they were on the stage of the social club, and trying on their costumes. It was an evening rather more boisterous than usual, and Peter was having trouble trying to keep order. Now Peter only had one eye; it was something that only Roger and very few others knew. Peter had lost the other eye as a child with measles, and since then had worn a matching glass eye. For the casual observer it was not at all obvious, and most of the team rehearsing did not know. Suddenly, as they all stood around laughing about their costumes, someone in the wings accidentally dropped a heavy weight on the floor, it fell with a large bang. The whole stage shook, Peter gave an involuntary jump and his glass eye flew out, bounced on the floor and started rolling down the slope towards the front of the stage. This was a shock to them all, and there was a sudden silence as everyone stared at the rolling eyeball. They had never seen the likes of it before and no one knew what to say. Peter however, with complete nonchalance, calmly caught it, polished it with his handkerchief and popped it back in again. After that, rehearsals went pretty smoothly.

Towards the end of the evening, as they were packing their chosen costumes away, someone called out in a voice of astonishment "Look at Joe!" Everyone turned to see Joe — he was the leading actor playing the part of Bully Bottom the weaver — and he was leaning against a pillar with a bowler hat on his head, his fingers in his mouth, and blowing furiously at his closed fingers. His cheeks were already puffed right out, and his face was turning bright red with the strain.

"What on earth," began Peter, but as they watched, the bowler hat on Joe's head slowly rose up about two inches higher across his forehead. Joe then opened his mouth, gasping out a great lung full of air and the bowler hat promptly fell back again. He then started to do it again, and everyone began to realise that Joe, always a real comic, had cleverly lodged the back brim of the hat against the pillar, and as he blew, he was gently leaning back a little and tipping the front of the bowler hat up in the air. Joe repeated a third time, taking no notice of the group, and the serious attitude on his face, his puffed out cheeks and look of desperate concentration was enough to cause the whole group to fall about laughing.

To cap it all, one of the cast, still in his rustic costume and practising his quite ghastly rustic accent, said solemnly, "Make Oi Larff!" and paused a second. "Make Oi Pee Oiself." He paused again "Make Oi tin leg rusty!" he finished.

More hilarious laughter followed and Roger thought, as he laughed, "This really is a great life! Work or play, there never seems to be a dull moment."

Roger could well say this, because apart from this drama venture, he was playing serious cricket all summer, helping to run the quarterly *Apprentices Journal*, teaching an advanced maths course at the technical college for one evening a week, playing chess some evenings, painting stage scenery for the drama group, and on top of all that, there was always something going on back at the Hall.

One Saturday, three weeks later, came the big day when Roger and the group, full of expectation, started out very early and travelled down by coach to the Fortune Theatre in London where the company drama festival was being held. There were fifteen groups presenting one-act plays. They came from widely different parts of the company and Sir Harry himself came along to open proceedings. Some of the groups were very professional, and the occasion was clearly an auspicious company event. After making themselves known, Roger, with the others, sat watching the early plays and listening to the generous applause many received at their final curtain. Roger swallowed hard. "In for a penny, in for a pound" he muttered to himself as they saw their turn coming nearer and nearer.

Finally, the time for their turn came. Roger and his merry band of amateurs, now in their rustic costumes, nervously entered the stage from the rear and hastily erected their set in the ten minute interval between plays. For the first time for all of them, this was a real theatre stage, and, as they prepared with the great glossy curtains closed in front of them, they could hear the general hum of the audience waiting on the other side, and their hearts were in their mouths. Roger, like most of the others, was silently wondering what the hell they had let themselves in for! At least they now knew their lines, and with Peter's quiet encouragement backstage, and with Joe's irrepressible humour, they were still full of nervous optimism. Suddenly their opening music of Mendelssohn's *Introduction to a Midsummer's Night's Dream* started, the curtains opened, and they were on!

Joe was in his element as Bully Bottom the bragging Weaver, and, as soon as the play started, he got a great laugh. After that, the going was easy, everyone remembered their lines and as they went along they knew they were doing very well.

"I see a voice!!! Now will I to the chink – to spy, and I can hear my Thisbe's face"
(Bully Bottom)

There were repeated great guffaws from the audience, and at the final curtain Roger felt the applause sounded the best of the day so far. They took their curtain bow feeling well pleased. When it came to the adjudicators summing up at the end of all the day, their optimism was well justified, the judge was most complimentary. He particularly praised the two principal characters, "Pyramus", played by Joe, and "Thisbe", his thwarted lover, played by Roger himself, as having been "Very funny indeed!" They all felt this was high praise coming from a professional, and when, in the final marking they found themselves placed right up second just behind the cup winner, their delight knew no bounds. Roger and crew were not only pleased but their smug satisfaction was enhanced by a professional member of the audience who complimented Peter afterwards. He thought their play had been the best production of the day!

That evening after a few well earned glasses of beer, there were high jinks coming home on the coach. One farcical incident occurred when the coach was held up in a London street by traffic congestion. The coach driver decided he needed to reverse a few yards, and shouted down to the back row "Is there anyone behind?" Now, after the day's success and still feeling full of fun, several looked out the back window and could see a London taxi right behind the coach, almost touching.

"All clear," they shouted out, and the driver started to reverse. Within two seconds there came an angry horn blast from behind the coach, and the back row, in high glee, saw the taxi being pushed backwards. Roger's coach stopped almost immediately, and the whole coach, in total abandonment roared with laughter as the taxi driver leapt out of his taxi, ran down towards the driver thumping the coach side in exasperation. Roger's driver sat there looking rather non-plussed as the taxi driver shouted up at him in broad cockney.

"D'yer want all the road to yourself mate?" He repeated this several times. "D'yer want all the road to yourself mate?" while Roger and the apprentices cheered. However, it turned out that no actual damage had been done, and after a few more angry exchanges between the two drivers, Roger's coach and the taxi drove off their different ways. The words "D'yer want all the road to yourself mate?" remained a catchphrase joke that was repeated time and time again on the long journey home until most of them fell asleep. It had been a long day.

Cricket had been a family tradition back at home for several generations, and Roger had played since he was six years old on the village green, and then in the local village team where his uncle was captain. He had kept up his cricket at university and it was therefore quite natural for him to immediately join the works cricket club as soon as the season started. He had been made very welcome, and there were now several other apprentices with him in the first eleven. In most of the sports organised by the social club, apprentices made a strong and important contribution to the teams, and the club played cricket regularly all through the summer in an excellent fixture list which consisted mainly of the other major firms in or near the city. The cricket was of high enough standard for many clubs to have full time professional groundsmen, and it was deliberately a non league group of friendly clubs. As well as the quality of the cricket, the refreshments during and after the games were usually very generous, and on one of these occasions Roger and the team got into a spot of trouble. Apart from the matches themselves, it was also a fairly regular habit for the cricket team to stop on the way home at a pub for a few jars of "the necessary" for after all, as the captain reasoned, a long afternoon's cricket on a hot day developed a generous thirst, particularly with the fast bowlers. Self-entertainment was then always the order of the day, and of course, it had to come from the apprentice contingent.

The team this day had unexpectedly won a good away match against a team that usually beat them, their opponents being a sister part of their own company in Coventry. There was always an extra element of inter-company rivalry in these games, and to crown it all, Roger himself had scored a half-century. The game had been close, and there was plenty to celebrate on the way home. They had left the opponents sports ground after a few friendly drinks with the vanquished, and were on the hour-long journey back home with plenty of robust singing filling the coach. However, as is the nature of these things, after the few beers they had already quaffed, a call of nature was demanded before they were more than halfway home, and a most convenient pub was spotted. They pulled up, the team promptly bailed out the coach, one or two having trouble negotiating the steps, and after attending to the necessary, they assembled around the saloon bar. The bar was already full with hardly a spare chair in the place, and once they were lined up, the captain called for a drink for Roger. After the drinks were served, the party propped up the bar and started another song. Their behaviour was completely respectable, and no-one minded. In fact several soon joined in. Roger was in very high spirits, and with his pint glass still three-quarters full, he plonked it down on the nearest table and produced his party trick.

Now Roger was particularly proud of this trick of his, he had learnt it when still in Sussex, and it required a certain amount of boldness and skill. He had first seen it performed on a music hall show and had practised it for hours at home outside in the garden until he had got it right. The trick consisted of grabbing hold of a glass of liquid with the palm of your hand reversed, picturing a full arc circle in your head, and then, holding the glass firmly, spinning it right round this arc and putting it back gently on to the table. At the top of the arc, and above your head, the glass was completely upside down but, due to the centrifugal force of the swinging circular movement, all the liquid would stay in the glass. Roger had now this down to a fine art, and could invert a pint of beer when it was still up to an inch from the top of being full. Roger proceeded to perform this trick smoothly and accurately several times in the pub, muttering silly incantations at the same time about casting a spell. He made it look so easy!

That was the trouble. At first several locals looked on in admiration, but it was getting late, and someone thought. "How simple, I can do that!" and proceeded to try. The new performer made a fundamental mistake right from the start, he grabbed the glass with his wrist the normal way round, and before Roger could shout, he had attempted to spin it over. With his hand that way round, when he got to the top of the arc, his wrist could not go any further, and the whole contents of the glass spewed out all over the table and his lady friend. Worse was to follow as several of his mates laughed and tried to do it themselves and the whole saloon carpet was soon starting to swim in spilled beer. The poor barman went purple, and the cricket team found themselves being shown the door in no uncertain manner. Still, they had had a really good day, and they sailed home in a wave of euphoria.

On another evening, at the end of a very hot day, the team had once again gathered afterwards at a pub and, just like tea breaks in the works, were idly chatting and laughing over a wide range of topics. Roger joined in and told them about some of the great inter-village matches he had enjoyed back in his early days back in Sussex. "We used to play one team," he began, "which had a cricket field up in the South Downs with a distinct slope right across the actual pitch. They had one quite old player, a very, very slow bowler, who threw up off breaks which bounced back down the slope, and he was a devil to play, we always seem to lose."

Another apprentice in the team interrupted. "You should have got down the pitch and knocked the hell out of him, that's what was needed."

"Just what I thought," said Roger. "I went in at third wicket down, and he got me out first ball. Stumped!"

Everyone laughed, and another team member joined in "That's funny you should say that! I was down in Sussex once," he said, "and was persuaded to join in a local village game, but we had to travel to it in the back of the butcher's van."

"Charming," said Roger "you must have smelt wonderful."

"Well, it was holiday time, and I couldn't say no," he continued, "but on the way home, after a lovely afternoon and several rounds at the village pub afterwards we were coming home in high spirits. The butcher was driving, and he had a practical joke sometimes of going over one of your famous Sussex hump-backed bridges as fast as he could, causing his passengers to fly up off their arses and end up sprawled in a heap."

"Very funny," said someone and they all laughed.

"But this time was once too often," the story teller continued. "He had more of us in the back than usual and we were all singing away when he came to the bridge. He flew over the bridge as fast as he dare, landed with a great crash, and his back axle broke! We had to be towed home by a tractor."

Roger and the team howled with laughter, and once again, Roger felt himself warmed with the beer and in great company. Life really was great.

A few days later there occurred an incident that brought Roger and his colleagues down to earth with a real bump. One of the apprentices at the Hall was a resident from Australia named John. He was a few years older than Roger's group, but was a very popular figure throughout the works and had been elected chairman of the Apprentices association. He was an imposing character accentuated by his unusual height. He was six feet four inches tall, and very big all round, but very athletic and a pillar of strength in the first fifteen rugby team. It was rumoured that he came from an important Australian family and was wealthy.

The night before the incident, Roger and a few others were sitting with John after supper in the Hall and he was chatting to them about how great life was in Australia. After the usual few pleasantries from the listeners — for example, that they wouldn't qualify for emigration as none had a criminal record — John casually mentioned his home. "A fairly large cattle area in North Australia in the outback," he volunteered in his very likeable Australian accent. Roger's group were suitably impressed.

"How big, John?" someone asked and John thought for a moment, "Waaall, I guess it's getting on for a million acres," he said without any trace of showing off and the listeners were even more impressed. There was silence for a minute.

"What do you do for entertainment when you're stuck out there in the sticks?" he was asked.

"That's never a problem," said John easily. "If we want a day off, we just pop down to Sydney and enjoy ourselves, it's only a thousand miles!"

His questioner swallowed, but was not to be put off, "and I suppose you have your own plane to fly you back from Sydney to your front gate?"

"Sroit," came the careful answer, "and then there's another plane takes us from the front gate up to the front door." Roger and the rest roared with laughter, but John kept a serious face, and no one was quite sure whether to believe him or not.

The shock to Roger came the next day. He was walking out of the ETO when he met John coming in, and was just starting some pleasantry when the look on John's face stopped him dead. John's face was the colour of chalk, his unseeing eyes staring to the front with a rigid set of deep lines on his face. He stared straight through Roger and strode past him without a word into the offices. Roger was very taken aback as John was always so friendly with everyone. Roger worried about this all the morning, but after lunch the reason became common gossip all around the factory. John had been to see his fellow Australian friend studying at the university for a further degree. His friend, a New Zealander, was finding the course very difficult and getting depressed. When John arrived at the university hall of residence, he was greeted with the news that his friend had just been found hanged in his room and was dead. It took Roger and all of them several days to recover their usual good spirits, and Roger himself could picture the situation only too well. There were several students in his evening class who had returned from their wartime service, and were studying desperately hard to catch up their lost years. They had become rusty compared with younger lads straight from sixth form at school, and Roger knew they often spent hours and hours on their homework. Roger often had to spend time with them, and from now on he resolved to give them all the time in the world.

One day Roger was seated in a quiet back room in the ETO with the editor of the apprentices' magazine and two other faithful contributors. One was Peter, an ex-editor himself, and the other was a very cheerful newcomer called David. They were studying the proposed cover design for the next issue. The magazine was a regular and popular offering from the apprentices, with full management encouragement, and was properly printed by the Publicity Department. It had a wide circulation including to other parts of the company and had a good reputation for being reasonably funny and a good read. The next issue was the "Spring" number, and the front cover artist, a faithful ex-"ape" now in the drawing office was also present and explaining his proposal to the assembled group. "It's an heraldic shield" he said "depicting spring time with an engineering twist."

"Go on," said the editor peering at the drawing on the table.

"On top left, that's 'Dexter Chief' in heraldic terms, you have a frisky lamb, and in the top right, 'Sinister Chief', you see the lamb leaping up in the air and cracking his head on the top of the shield. 'Dexter Base,' then shows him spark out on the grass, and finally, in 'Sinister Base', you see a plate of roast lamb on the table. Around the top are the usual crossed spanners, and the motto underneath says 'Per Ardua ad Nutrimens'. That is a corny crib which means, I hope, 'by strenuous work we achieve dinner'." He paused and waited for the table's comments, "I thought we could make a short article about it inside," he added hopefully.

"Not bad!" grunted Peter, "but a bit complicated, and this drawing of the slices of roast lamb looks more like a cow-pat."

"Thanks very much!" grumbled the disgruntled artist as they all laughed.

Roger joined in, "I'm not really sure of the motto, and by the way, I believe 'Dexter' means 'right'. You know, as in dexterous for right handed, but you are calling this the left?"

"Aha," beamed the artist grinning, "that's caught you! The heraldic definitions are based on the image of the shield as seen by the holder himself from behind his shield, not by a viewer from the front!"

"Good Lord" thought Roger, "Switchgear meter panel confusion all over again!"

"Come on," interrupted the editor, "enough of this academic stuff, let's keep to the business. We are up against time as usual, publicity need our final copy by the end of the week, and we're nowhere ready yet!"

"How about" said David after a pause, "we change the bottom left to a bottle of mint sauce, and the last corner to crossed knives and forks?"

"How the hell do I draw a recognisable bottle of mint sauce in such a tiny space?" exploded the artist. There was silence for a few minutes.

"OK, OK," said the editor. "I like the basic idea of the mint sauce and this is my suggestion. We simply draw a little conical bottle with a leaf on the front as the sauce bottle, use the knife and fork idea, and change the motto to simple English 'He Mint Well'." Groans and a laugh all round greeted this horrible pun, but everyone basically thought it was pretty good, and the artist was sent away to make the changes. He said his section leader often grumbled that he spent more time on cartoons for the journal than he ever did on his work, but no one else apparently seemed to mind.

"Now," continued the editor, shuffling through a pile of papers, "as usual, we have a number of really good cartoons, and almost enough hard script, but we need a few more words to balance the journal up."

Roger cautiously put forward a suggestion, "I've just had a new item given to me that I think is reasonable," he said and plonked a tatty piece of paper on the table.

"Thank you, but before we look at it" said the editor," I have one here that I think between us we can polish up and use. It's a proposed series of short 'agony aunt' letters that the proverbial Aunt Aggie has to answer.

"We've done that before" said Peter, "but we can always do it again."

"Right" said the editor reading his papers, "try this. Number one"

"Dear Aunt Aggie, I am a bit worried about my boyfriend, I love him lots, bur every time we meet he gives me a bar of soap. "For a little present" he says. I now have 179 bars and he still keeps giving them to me. What shall I do? Yours faithfully, "Perplexed"

"Dear Perplexed, If I were you, the next time he gives you a bar, just turn round and stick.....Yours, Aunt Aggie."

The editor interrupted his reading "I would simply propose to stop there. Our readers will guess the rest. Do you agree?"

"Absolutely," laughed Peter "or else you won't get it through our own management censors."

"Here's another" continued the editor, "the same sort of idea."

"Dear Aunt Agatha, I was well brought up, but I am now getting very distressed at the foul language some of my companions consistently use in front of me in Big Shop. Every instruction they give me is always laced with 'f..in' and 'blindin' adjectives. If I have a quiet word with them, will it do any good? Yours sincerely, 'Pious.'"

"Dear Pious, Not a b————- bit of good. Yours, Aunt Aggie."

Peter suddenly interrupted, he was reading Roger's tatty piece of paper and started to laugh "This is really clever" he said "I do like this. Try this for size. It's a nice parody on Wordsworth's famous poem about daffodils. I must read it to you."

"Go on then," sighed the editor' "It looks as though mine will have to wait," and Peter read out the poem in his best stage voice.

> "I wandered hazy as a cloud, among my many
>   aches and ills,
> I felt that I may need a shroud, at least a box of Beechams
>   pills,
> Pleading for a welcome snooze, I roundly cursed all bottled
>   booze.
>
> We vowed we'd had a super time, I never really meant to stay.
> The stars had long began to shine, before we made our
>   homeward way,
> Watching the elephants start to prance, flapping their wings in
>   sprightly dance.
>
> The lamp-posts by them danced, and they, outdid the
>   elephants in glee.
> You think we were a trifle gay? We were a jocund company,
> We sang and danced, but little thought, what evils all these
>   symptoms brought.
>
> For oft, when on my couch I lie, with my head aching fit to
>   burst,
> I ponder with a bloodshot eye, about the terrors of my thirst. And then
> my gut with poison fills, and empties o'er the
>   daffodils.

Everyone in the room applauded and Peter was full of praise "It looks as though we've found some new talent at last," he said. "This man could become our, 'Poet Laureate' if we encourage him."

And so the meeting went on all the afternoon until at last

everyone was satisfied and the journal was finally put to bed for another three months.

A few weeks later, Roger sat alone with a problem. The year before, at the apprentices' annual dinner, he had volunteered to write the script for the after-dinner entertainment. He had agreed, had written a script, and after a few crazy weeks rehearsing, the show had been a wonderful success. The dinner was the highlight of the apprentices' year and was always attended by most of the local works' top management, together with usually one or two from the company's central London office. Most apprentices also attended giving a total attendance of several hundred and the main hall of the social club was always full. Roger's script last year had been born after he had been talked into writing it by Peter from the drama society, following their successes together in writing funny sketches at Hall parties. It was a year later now, and Roger's problem was that, human nature being what it is, everyone had unanimously declared that this year only Roger could write the new script, and here he was being left alone to get on with it! He was tempted to repeat Skipper's famous remark on one occasion to the managing director, "It isn't quite like shovelling s..t you know", but he knew no-one would believe him.

Roger sat remembering last year's show. After a cautious start at rehearsals it had ended up as a joyful amalgam of apprentices' high spirits. Some apprentices were very talented, some were very amateur but as keen as mustard, and many had very good voices. There had been an excellent pianist, plus a few injections of extra good ideas once rehearsals had got under way. One vivid extra cameo had been put in by Lyn, a burly New Zealand apprentice who was a rugby fanatic. There was one scene set in the jungle, and Lyn introduced the New Zealand rugby chant the "Haka". He trained half a dozen equally burly individuals to dress as traditional Maoris, and they gave a most vociferous rendering, glaring fiercely out at the audience from the stage. The spectacle was quite new at the time, and the applause afterwards was tremendous. The theme of the show had been the company's worldwide search for new apprentices, and this had given a lot of scope for all sorts of corny gags and elaborate sets that had been put together by a willing back-stage group. Apprentices were an inventive breed! Roger had also utilised the many musical talents in the cast by incorporating a number of Gilbert and Sullivan and other popular songs and dubbing fresh words. The show got away to a good start with one of them.

As the curtains opened, a talented member of the cast entered dressed as the Apprentice Manager Mr Rollason, or "Rolly", and indeed he looked rather like him in his make-up, and he could also imitate the manager's gestures to a tee. He had been quietly studying them for weeks. He came in strumming a guitar, the last thing in the world one could imagine Rolly actually doing, and he burst into song to the tune of "A wandering minstrel I" from the *Mikado*.

> *A wandering supervisor I, a thing of beauty,*
> > *I always do my duty, and bring new apprentices in.*
> *Although I travel half across the world to find 'em,*
> > *I nearly always blind 'em*
> *With my wonderful e-e-eeloquence"* (repeat)

Roger smiled to himself, "Yes it had been a great start," and after that the tempo had never seemed to slacken. Another big hit had been a duet by two landladies. Landladies were the curse of apprentices forced to live in digs, and the audience howled with delight when two grotesquely dressed "landladies" came on front stage during a scene shift and sang a duet to the tune of Offenbach's "Bold Gendarmes."

> (primo) *We're public guardians bold yet wi-iry,*
> > (secondo) *And of ourselves we take good care,*
> (p)*We're all in Mrs Mason's di-ary,*
> > (s) *But if she calls we're never there.*
> (p) *"But if we find a young appre-entice,*
> > (s)*A lad who don't know what the trade is,* (dance)
> (p)*"We take'em in,*
> > (s) *"We take 'em in,*
> (p) *"We take 'em in*
> (duet forttissimo) *"We take 'em in, we show them we're the*
> > *bold landladies."* (dance)

Roger's mind went back and smiled. The pair had been an outrageous sight, singing together in perfect close harmony, waving their rolling pins instead of truncheons, and Mrs Mason, the very popular works personnel manager, was sitting on the top table and nearly having an apoplexy. It wasn't helped when one landlady lifted her skirt to scratch her muscular thigh with the rolling pin, and exhibited a great expanse of vivid, well padded out, purple bloomers. At the end of the last verse, poor Mrs Mason was holding on to her neighbour crying with laughter with a handkerchief pushed in her mouth.

> (p) At *breakfast time we are most so-ociable,*
>> (s) And *then our service knows no limit,*
> (p) *We put the jam pot on the ta-able,*
>> (s) Provided that there's no jam in it
> (p) *But if they do not seem to se-ee it,*
>> (s) *Or ask us where the marmalade is?*
> (p) *We chuck 'em out,*
>> (s) *We chuck 'em out,*
> (p) *We chuck 'em out*
> (duet, FF) *We chuck 'em out we show them we're the bold landladies"*.
> (Exit to martial music, raised truncheons, and funny march)

Roger also remembered one gag in the script that he was still quite proud of. At one point, a very green apprentice had unfortunately criticised the works' tea and been shot dead by a fanatic. This lead to a coroner's inquest;

> (Coroner) *The case is closed, I am recording a verdict of "Death by natural causes."*
> (Observer) *But that's crazy! He was shot dead by a hail of bullets!*
> (C, imperturbably) *Quite right! He had six bullets in him. If he hadn't have died it would have been most un-natural.*

There had been a few groans amid the laughs, but after all, it had been at the end of the dinner with plenty of beer and wine still flowing and, as Roger thought wistfully. "There are times when anything goes!" Now, with a clean sheet of paper in front of him, and a sober mind, everything looked very different.

The next exercise to tax Roger's mind was the forthcoming Christmas Ball at the Hall. It would be Roger's last one in residence, as his apprenticeship would finish in the coming summer, and he himself would be cast out to join the dwellers in digs. Mrs Mason had already warned him she could find plenty of landladies who would do justice to Roger's song at the dinner and Roger had detected a merry twinkle in her eye. But for the moment, a working party had assembled to plan the coming Ball, and David, a fellow resident started off by enquiring who had kept the "Notice for the stairs"?

Roger looked at him scornfully. "You mean that corny old joke notice that reads 'FIRE REGULATION—NO NAKED FLAMES PERMITTED IN THE BEDROOMS?' That seems to come out every time we have ladies invited for a do!"

"That's the one" replied David, "we always put that up, it's tradition."

"Tradition my foot!" replied Roger, "it's corny, can't we think of something new? I've seen it up about four times since I joined, and even the notice itself *looks* old and tatty by now."

You'll find the Hall a buffer between you and the rough industrial world.

Peter from the drama festival success was present. He was a regular guest at hall "dos" ever since his earlier days as an apprentice himself, and he hastened to explain the background to Roger.

"A few years ago," explained Peter, "the heating in this old Hall was diabolical, and many apprentices used to grumble, but installing full central heating was, of course, going to be a major investment in a large old hall like this. As a result, not much was done for years and the bedrooms in particular were pretty icy in winter. Several apprentices solved the problem in their own rooms by bringing in electric fires, but this was strictly illegal for obvious reasons."

"We never had a warm bedroom at home," shrugged Roger, "we just used to dive in, wriggle like mad for a few minutes and then snuggle down as warm as toast."

"You don't know what cold is," laughed David. "In my home in Canada where you get temperatures of minus thirty degrees, wriggling like that wouldn't do any good at all, more like your toes would fall off with frost-bite!"

"To continue!" said Peter glaring at the interrupters. "Many of the apprentices didn't have much money, and home-made devices started to appear. One quite successful device was to mount a forty watt lamp bulb inside a biscuit tin, knock a few holes in the tin and plug the contraption into the electric light socket before supper. Come bedtime, the bed was lovely."

"Bit risky?" questioned Roger.

"Maybe," shrugged Peter "but in the end it led to trouble. One boffin type, nailed two pieces of broom handle at each end of a tin lid so that they stuck up like two posts, and suspended a one kilowatt electric fire element between them. The nearest power point was in the corridor just outside his door, and he used to plug into that in the evenings and the mornings, and it worked very well."

"Was it insulated?" asked Roger.

"Of course it wasn't, just bare connections each end and the bare element itself on the middle!"

All present sat there just picturing the scene. "That couldn't last for long!" said someone.

"That's right!" finished Peter. "It didn't, the lad left it still plugged in one morning by mistake, rushed off to catch the works bus, and a cleaner found it."

"What happened then?"

"The cleaner almost had hysterics, she refused to go into the room, and Rolly was called out of a meeting at the works' and rushed home to see what was going on." Another old hand took up the tale.

"The upshot was a bloody nuisance," he said. "Rolly called in the works' police and they did a search of all bedrooms. All such contraptions, including proper electric fires were confiscated, and," he paused to grin, "some residents were also very embarrassed about other things that came to light. But enough said about those." He laughed and continued. "That evening, Rolly had all residents on the mat, read the riot act, and a fire officer gave them a lecture about the dangers of such activities in such an old precious building."

Peter then finished the tale. "The result was this notice about 'No naked flames' appeared next day, and has been kept as a souvenir ever since". They all laughed.

"And what about the heating?" queried Roger.

"That got sorted as well before the next winte.r "God works in a mysterious way his wonders etcetera, etcetera," quoted Peter as a winding up statement. "Now, for goodness sake, let's get down to this Christmas party."

There had been some major building repairs in the Hall that autumn, as some dry rot had been discovered under one of the upstairs bathrooms, and this was still a hot topic of conversation. Peter now produced a suggested song that listed all Rolly's woes, finishing with this latest saga. It went to the tune of "The Policeman's Lot" from *Pirates of Penzance,* and he sang it out to the group, finishing with;

> *Now I hope you will excuse my bitter feeling,*
>   (chorus) *Bitter feeling*
> *But it's rather apt to spoil a wardens' fun*
>   (chorus) *Warden's fun*
> *When he finds the toilets coming through the ceiling*
>   (chorus) *Through the ceiling.*
> *"Ooooooh! a warden's lot is not an nappy one!*
>   (Chorus) *Nappy one(repeat)*

They all thought this was great. They always had a sing-song at the end of the evening, and this would fit in nicely. But the real problem was to hit on a theme for the evening in which everyone could join in, and after much further and rather long-winded argument, an elaborate plan was finally agreed.

"Now," said Peter sounding a trifle exhausted, let's run over the final plan again. "The theme is to be that the Hall is haunted, and I will announce this to the guests early on in the evening, right?"

"That's it!" nodded David.

"Probably as soon as the coach party of nurses arrive and we are all having the first warm-up drink of hot punch."

"Now you, Roger, are going to be the main ghost, and you will keep popping up at odd places during the evening and doing your best to scare people, right?"

"That's it," said Roger. "I shall drift out of dark corners in a white sheet with a skull mask on and make appropriate moaning noises."

"You don't need a mask to frighten people" smirked David.

"Ha, ha," grunted Peter, "For goodness sake let's stick to the point, it's getting late!"

"Sorry," grinned David, "what next?"

Peter then continued. "At some time later, after supper, I shall ask if anyone has seen the ghost, and if so, where, and Roger will flutter in and out behind me, and like the old pantomime gag, as I turn to look at, you will disappear, but immediately seem to appear at the other end of the room."

"That's it," said Roger. "Jim wants to join in, and he will be the second apparition, dressed the same as me, and we will do a sort of 'Tweedle-Dee, Tweedle-Dum' act between us". "Will you practise that?" asked Peter.

"No problem," grinned Roger, "leave that to us."

"No chance," said Peter curtly. "I will come in tomorrow and the three of us can try it out together."

"OK, OK, if you really think we need to, but some things work best if they are just spontaneous you know."

"I know all too bloody well!" sighed Peter. "If apprentices can cock a thing up, they usually do!"

"No chance with this one," said Roger in a slightly smug voice, and the others round just raised their eyebrows and grinned.

There was a pause, "The finale's the tricky bit, isn't it?" said David.

"Yes" agreed Peter, "and it will need good timing. I'm coming to that now. You, David, together with two or three more, will burst into the hall late in the evening just before the final carol singing, announcing triumphantly that you have caught the ghost! You will then lead in Roger, still dressed as the ghost of course with a rope round his neck, right?"

"Correct," agreed David. "And then you Peter, are going to cook up some fancy words, a sort of verdict for all his crimes, and announce that the ghost will now be hanged in front of everyones' very eyes in the rear courtyard."

"Yes," confirmed Peter, "and also explain that once hung we need to cut his head off in front of everyone, using a silver sword, in order to ensure he never comes back again." "Fine," said Roger sounding a bit concerned. "But I'm the ghost! Now how exactly will you hang me?"

"I've started on that," confirmed David. "We shall have two apprentices' cars facing into the floodlit courtyard, with a platform across the top, and a gallows tree behind ready for the rope. We will lead you up on to the platform, get the rope in position, and get the audience, who will by then we hope all be in the yard, to chant a countdown. As we reach zero, we shall douse the two floodlights in the courtyard, and the cars will switch on their headlights to blind the audience. That will allow you to quickly dive unseen under the platform. Your part is then finished, and we get to the great finale!"

"Which is?" asked Peter." It will be Jim, the other ghost, still in his costume simultaneously appearing up in the turret on the roof and he will lean out as far as he can, and give a great cackle of demonic sounding triumphant laughter and then also disappear as well!."

"Good, that's fine," said Peter getting up to go home. "It's late, I'm tired, let's hope it all it goes to plan."

Roger was still thinking and turned to David. "Whose cars will you use? I'm just thinking we've got about six wrecks here in the stables that apprentices keep tinkering with. Are you sure two will be in a good enough state for the do?"

"Don't worry!" said David. "But there's one we shan't use, and that's 'the Bomb', you know that old London taxi that's becoming a byword for trouble." He started to laugh "Chas took it into the city last week with his new girlfriend and her chum in the back. He had to stop outside the bank to get some money, and he explained to the girls that he would have to leave the engine running as he would never start it again if it stopped, but said he wouldn't be a minute."

Peter laughed "Go on!," he said grinning, "I haven't heard this one."

Well, Chas went into the bank, bang in the city centre, parking 'the Bomb' right outside the bank, leaving the engine running. This of course caused immediate suspicion to everyone passing by. Inside the bank there was unfortunately a queue, and Chas was gone what seemed like ages to the two girls, who just sat huddled down in the deep back seat explaining to one suspicious person after another that there was nothing wrong, the driver would be back in a minute. It wasn't helped by the big notice that is painted across the back of the old taxi saying 'DON'T LAUGH, IT MIGHT BE YOUR DAUGHTER IN THE BACK!' The girls said afterwards they could have died!" Peter and the rest all laughed at the recollection, and split up to prepare for the big day.

The Monday after the party, Peter was in his drawing office telling his colleagues all about the party at the Hall and he gave them an outline of the ghost plan that had been performed.

"Crazy buggers!" said his neighbour grinning.

"Well, actually it went very well to start with" continued Peter. "In fact it caused a lot of fun right up to the point where they had to hang the ghost."

"What then?" someone asked.

"They hoisted the ghost up on to the scaffold, hung the rope round his neck and over the gallows, and went through the countdown with the guests laughing and joining in. They were all wondering what would happen next, while Roger the ghost, still with his white sheet and skull mask on kept making horrible cackling laughs, anticipating the "denouement" when his double would suddenly re-appear up in the turret". Peter rolled out the word "denouement" with great relish.

"I bet something went wrong!" said a listener.

"You're right" laughed Peter. "As the count-down reached 'zero', the flood-lights went out, the car lights blazed up as planned, and the second ghost, Jim, appeared in the lighted turret as planned. But instead of demoniacal triumphant laughter, he leaned out, with his mask off, shouting in a very human voice, "David come and help! I've broken my ankle!"

Peter's audience reacted with a mixture of laughter and concern. "Had he?" they asked.

"Yes", said Peter. "In his rush to get up the very narrow winding stair to the turret, he had tripped over his sheet and fallen quite badly. We found him laying on the turret floor with his ankle swelling up like a balloon, and it was a very difficult job to get him up and carry him down the narrow winding stair again. How he had ever made it up the rest of the stair to keep his part in the show we shall never know."

"Good for him" approved the listeners, "what happened to the party?"

"It sort of recovered," said Peter. "Two of the nurses examined Jim's ankle and agreed it probably wasn't broken, just badly strained, and he was packed off to his bed where he lay cursing, and listening to the final carol singing down below, and the evening finished off OK".

LIFE AT CASTLE BROMWICH HALL.

"I'm sorry old man — you'll have to go — you've already been here longer than anybody."

As Roger's final year as an "Ape" drew to its close, there were a number of his colleagues also planning their next step. One or two were going off to do deferred National Service; David was off back to Canada; the lad whose Morgan had fallen in half was joining Outside Erection; another close friend was joining the turbo-generator design office, and the irrepressible Joe had been grabbed by Sales and was off to Brazil to boost the company's strong business growth in that country. Roger himself was staying on at Witton with a position as assistant to the Works Consulting Engineer, Dr Friedlander, with whom he had already worked on several occasions. However, that time had not yet arrived, the Hall group still had a few weeks to go as apprentices, and they decided that, as one final fling together, they would have a grand Saturday night sing-song at one of their favourite local pubs in the village.

That Saturday evening arrived, and things started off, as they usually did, with a few rounds of drinks and general chatter with the many friends they had now made. The pub was full and there was the usual quiet hum of conversation. After a while, Joe turned to Roger and said, "Come on Roger! The place is as dead as a doornail, get on the piano and we'll give 'em a song to wake 'em up". Roger did not consider himself a qualified pianist, but he was self-taught enough to knock out songs with plenty of gusto and they had started many a pub sing-song together over the past two years. Roger sat down with Joe standing beside him and they cracked off with "Keep the home fires burning". They had started with this number on many occasions before, and it always went down well. Joe was a serious amateur singer, still taking regular singing lessons and had a very good baritone voice. As usual, most of the chatter stopped, and Joe became the centre of attention. All the apprentices with them joined in the choruses as they followed with many of their regular pot-boilers, "The White Cliffs of Dover", "Lilli Marlene", "Run rabbit run", "Bless 'em all", "When the Saints go marching in", "'A Nightingale sung in Berkley Square". Roger knew them all by heart, these war-time songs were still very popular and it wasn't long before everybody in the pub was joining in with gusto.

Joe by now had a captive audience, and he began to include some of his favourite old-time music hall solos. He was very fond of these, and could sing the verses as well as any professional. He had magic timing, perfect innuendos, and a wonderful clarity in even the most tongue-twisting numbers like "When Father papered the parlour". He was always in great demand. By now the evening was approaching closing time, and the air was getting noisy and some of the songs inevitably went rather on the blue side. Suddenly, after a full rendering of the old, very suggestive rugby song "Roll me Over", Joe stopped. "Ladies and Gentlemen," he said, "and also everybody here," he announced, getting a cheap laugh. "For your further entertainment, I now call upon our pianist Roger to desist from tinkling the ivories, and tell us some of his corny country jokes!" He paused for a few seconds, "He comes from Sussex," he added, as though this explained it, and got another good laugh.

Joe had never done such a trick on Roger before, and for a second or two, Roger could hardly believe his ears. "Give him a big hand," Joe prompted the audience, at the same time grinning broadly at poor Roger who now found himself staggering to his feet completely at a loss for words. It was getting near the end of the evening and the audience, many well into their cups, encouraged Roger with a great cheer! Roger himself was feeling quite mellow by now as well, and he decided to go along with Joe, he would murder him afterwards! However, he was in it now up to his neck, so he gathered his wits hastily and decided to have a go.

Roger started with one of his old country favourites. "Right then, here we go. One day, old farmer William walked across to his neighbouring farm and spoke to farmer George," and Roger put on his best rustic accent for the speech bits. 'Garge! Wot did yer gi' your 'orse when 'e were ill?', 'Oi gi' moi 'orse turpentine,' said George. 'Thankee,' said William and went back to his farm." Roger got a laugh with the word "turpentine" which was all the encouragement he needed, so he pressed on. "About a month later, William met up with George again 'Garge!' he said, 'Did you zay you gi'd your 'orse turpentine when 'e were ill?', 'Aaaarh!' said George. 'Wal', said William, 'Oi gi'd moi 'orse turpentine and 'e died!'." This got quite a laugh, and Roger paused to get a dramatic effect, and then finished. "George shook his head sadly. 'Aaaarh' he said, "zo did moin'." Great hoots of laughter greeted the end, Roger considered this quite a daft joke, but he had used it with good effect for many years, "The old ones are the best ones," he used to say to himself.

Roger had noticed three ladies sitting at the back with large glasses of cider in front of them and who were obviously hugely enjoying themselves, especially any songs that had been a little suggestive! Roger had just the joke for them, it had been told him by an old country labourer back in Sussex, so he now plunged in. "Now, there was this country fair going on one day where one of the side shows was a 'test your strength' machine. You had to pick up a mallet, and hit down on the end of a lever as hard as you could. The other end of the lever propelled a wooden block up a slide towards a big bell at the top. If you hit the lever hard enough, the block could shoot right to the top of the slide and strike the bell with a large clang." Roger paused, he could sense that everyone understood, so he pressed on. "Now there was a strong young lad there who had a go at the machine, and hit the bell three times in a row and he was declared the champion. For a prize he was given a live young goose in a sack. A live goose was a real present of course, it would be his family's Christmas dinner that year. It was a good prize so the lad needed to look after it carefully." Roger was going to spin this joke out as long as he could. He was in a quandary of how on earth he would be able to follow this one up.

"Now this young lad, like many country lads, was wearing an old pair of his father's trousers, they were much too big for him, and were kept up by a stout length of string round his waist." The three girls immediately thought this was very funny and gave a great hoot of laughter, so Roger knew he was on to a winner. "Well, the lad didn't know how best to carry the goose around all the afternoon, so he stuffed it, still inside the sack, down the front of his trousers where there was plenty of room." The girls and many others thought this was hilarious, and for a minute Roger couldn't continue for the noise. "Come the evening," continued Roger, "the lad, at a bit of a loose end so to speak, went to the pictures where he settled down in a comfortable seat and became engrossed in the film. The young goose was still inside his trousers, but warm and comfortable and sound asleep." The three girls, and many others were tittering in curiosity as to what on earth was going to happen next, and Roger was thoroughly enjoying himself.

"A little later on two girls came in and took the two seats right next to the lad, and started to munch away on great bags of crisps each. But by now the poor old goose was getting hot and had woken up. It started to wriggle away, and a few minutes later had wormed its head out of the sack, and out through the lad's trouser flies. It started to wave its head and long neck around." Roger sensed that some of the audience had guessed this already, but the laughter was great all the same. He continued. "One of the girls next to the lad glanced down and spotted it in the dim light and nearly froze with terror. She turned to her friend, and said, 'Martha! Martha!' This lad next to me, he's flashin' it'. Martha just shrugged, 'Just don't take any notice Annie, such men are 'armless.' But Annie wasn't satisfied. 'Do 'ave a look Martha,' she pleaded.' 'I don't want to look,' said Martha, 'Once you've seen one, you've seen the lot!'

The three girls in the pub curled up with laughter at this, and one at the end slapped the man next to her across his knee and they snuggled closer together laughing. "'Well, I bet you've never seen one like this,' said Annie,'it's eating my crisps!'.'"

"Bull's eye," thought Roger to himself as the whole audience erupted in laughter.

Joe came to Roger's rescue. "Thank you very much Roger, I think that's enough of your jokes for now. "No wonder they say 'Zilly Zussex'," he added to a laugh.

Roger just grinned and sat back at the piano, He would put him right about "Silly Sussex" later. He knew that the correct expression was Scilly Sussex, referring to the reputation for flowers similar to the Scilly Isles.

"Now," said Joe, "it's getting near closing time, but there's time for a few more songs, any suggestions?"

Someone shouted out "The Wild West Show". Roger swallowed hard, this was one of the more crude songs usually reserved for male-only company on coach trips after rugby or cricket matches, but it was late in the evening and Joe wasn't at all put out, he knew his audience and the landlord, and could judge these things to a nicety. "Right!" he said, "you all sing the choruses and I'll try and remember the zoo keeper's patter in between". He started them off with the chorus;

> "*We're off to see the wild west show, the elephant and the
> kanger-ooooo,
> Never mind the weather, never mind the rain, we're off to see
> the wild west show*".

It was obvious that many knew the song very well, and the singing was loud and boisterous. Joe supplied the descriptions between verses, he was a little careful in his selection of verses, and after a few came out with one of Roger's favourites. Joe put on a comic, high-pitched voice with added "h"s wherever it sounded ridiculous and shouted:

> "*Now here. Ladies and gentlemen, on the left, we have the many spotted le-o-pard. This hanimal is hinteresting, as hit his covered with spots. It has one spot for every day of the year!*"

One of the audience knew the correct cue. "What about leap years?" he shouted out and Joe was ready:

> "*Keeper! Kindly lift up the le-o-pard's tail and show this good lady the twenty-ninth of February*".

After much laughter the boisterous chorus repeated, and Roger, tinkling away merrily, wondered what Joe would dare come up with next. He swallowed hard as Joe started, he knew what was coming.

> "*And here we have the unique hEgyptian camel. This hanimal is the honly hanimal hin the world with a tri-hangular harsehole. It heats cement and shits bricks and hence the pyramids.*"

Pandemonium broke out, everyone was crying with laughter and no-one seemed in the least offended!

As the laughter died down, there was an interruption from the audience.

"What about the sexual urge of the camel?" a voice called out. Joe was a bit non-plussed, but only for a second.

"Sexual urge?" he queried, "I can't imagine a camel having a sexual urge. If he tried to get his leg over, he would fall flat on his hump!" The image was so funny that Roger found himself roaring with laughter with the rest of them.

"You know" continued the speaker ignoring Joe, "that song to the tune of the Eton Boating song," and before anyone could say a word he started to sing:

> "*The sexual urge of the camel, is greater than anyone thinks.*
> "*And oft at the height of his passion, he is tempted to "bugger" the sphinx.*
> "*But the sphinx's sexual orifice, is blocked by the sands of the Nile.*
> "*Which accounts for the hump on the camel, and the sphinx's* inscrutable smile".

The singer was greeted with loud applause, especially from the many ladies who had not heard it before. No-one seemed in the least put out. Roger knew the verse of old, he had first heard it from Skipper who claimed it was one of the few smutty verses he approved. "It had class," he had said. "Good old Skipper" thought Roger, he had once told a group of them that there were only three sources of jokes in the world. "Shit, sex, and other's misfortunes." Ever since then, Roger had found this to be absolutely true!

Roger now felt he could also join in the general zany-ness. "Do you know what camel's eat," he asked.

"Go on," said Joe.

Roger smirked "He lives in the desert on the sand-which-is there."

Great groans all round greeted this awful pun, and Joe capped it by saying "Roger, get back to your Beano comic," and the general merriment continued.

Time was nearly up, and Joe led them in a set of rousing songs to finish off the evening. "The Lambeth walk" was followed by "There'll always be an England", "Kiss me goodnight Sergeant Major", and with the nostalgic final number "Now is the hour", they finally called it a day.

As Joe and his party were leaving, a man rose rather unsteadily to his feet and stopped them at the door. He grabbed Joe by the hand. "Thank you so much," he stammered, "thank you so much, you are all wonderful. I've been in both the wars, and I am now alone and feel depressed all the time. But you young lads" he said looking at them all, "you young lads have really cheered me up. For the first time for ages you have given me a bit of confidence in the future." He insisted on shaking hands with all of them one by one, saying over and over again "God bless you, God bless you!" and there were tears in his eyes.

Mr Rollason and the Hall apprentices in residence in 1952
(The author is second from left, back row)

APPENDIX 1

Approximate measurement guide. British Imperial

(To help picture some of the engineer's practical jargon in the '50s);

1 thous.	=	one thousandth of an inch, the smallest manual measurement in daily use in engineering fitting work. Approx. the thickness of cling film.
1 inch	=	the distance from the front of the index finger nail to the first knuckle.
1 foot	=	12 inches, the length of the human foot.
1 yard	=	3 feet, the distance of a man's step, or from the nose to the finger tips with the arm extended sideways.
1 fathom	=	2 yards, the full outstretched arm span (from the sailors playing out a plumb-line when sounding out the water depth under the boat).
22 yards	=	1 cricket pitch, easy to visualise.
1 furlong	=	220 yards, an old common agricultural distance in land measurements.

1 mile	=	8 furlongs or 1,760 yards.(A fit man would smartly walk 5 miles in an hour).
1 pint	=	A standard popular beer drinking measure, still retained.
1 gallon	=	8 pints, a standard bucket holds 2 gallons. (When drinking, a skinful?.)
1 bushel	=	8 gallons. (A common fruit picking measurement.)
1 pound	=	2 standard small pads of butter. Approx. the weight of 1 pint of water.
1 stone	=	14 pounds (lbs) (A 6 ft, slim man weighs around 12 stone)
1 cwt	=	112 pounds. The weight of a sack of grain, (1 hundred weight) a standard able man's carrying weight on the farm.
1 ton	=	20 cwt or 2,240 lbs. The largest general weight in general parlance on the shop floor. A substantial weight treated with respect. The weight of a solid lump of iron approx. 2 ft square by 3 ft long. (An elephant weighs 3 to 5 tons.)
1 kilowatt	=	1 kw ,or 4 amps at 240 volts. An electrical measurement of power, or the rate of doing work, equivalent

to 1.3 horsepower. In other words, a 3 kw fire would need 4 horses at full strength to generate this power (but whereas the fire can go on all day, the horses would be exhausted inside an hour or so).

1 kw hour,	=	1 kwh a unit of work done, ie 1kw for 1hour. The universal basis of charging.

The power of electricity is taken for granted, and often underrated. A salutary figure is that a modern coal fired power station typically has four steam generator sets of 500 MW, that is 2,000 MW in total, producing the workload of 2.7 million horses at full stretch all day. (Which rather puts a wind generator in perspective?)

APPENDIX 2

Letters from old apprentices

Author's note.

After the last Apprentices get-together in 1993, following the closure of the Witton works in 1969, I invited anyone with old memories to write to me, and some of their recollections are incorporated in the previous chapters. However, a great deal of detail is not included, and I attach their letters verbatim as many of them give an excellent picture of the spirit that ran right through the works, and is probably not found anywhere these days?

A2.1 Dick Langford, commercial apprentice, 1954–still batting.

I recall those magnificent Christmas Balls held at the Magnet Club; black tie, wonderful spread by Bill Corner's ladies, and an enormous cost for penniless apprentices. I refer to the 1958 event when Roger Boyle, the intrepid rugby forward from the valleys was the Social Secretary *(of the Apprentices Association)*. It was alleged that Roger's socks, by the way, hummed to the tune of "Land of my Father's". I myself was assistant treasurer at the time, with the responsibility of getting the show on the road, and collecting the Company subsidy,— —- for Friday, 19th December.

All was going well, the band, an 8 piece ensemble, was booked and the tickets were going well.

The scene changes to a Roger's digs in Slade Road, 7.00 pm Friday evening, 12th December.

The telephone rings and Roger picks up the receiver.

Voice: Rollason here *(Manager apprentice training)*

Roger: Bollocks. (suspecting an impersonation hoax)

Rollason: It's not bollocks, Boyle, Harry Engleman is at the Magnet Club waiting to play the first waltz. What are you going to do about it?

Roger: Bollocks. (his vocabulary was extended to full stretch)....Sir? (when the penny dropped)

Rollason: You had better get on your bike and get there as fast as you can and sort it out. (Early Tebbit syndrome)

Having frantically searched for the correspondence, and armed with sheer panic, the 16 stone Welshman pedalled his way to the fray.

Engleman, somewhat shamed-faced, admitted that it was his cock-up but as it was the Christmas season, he was booked up for the following Friday. As always with Apes pending disasters, all turned out well and Engleman sorted out a motley crew of relatives and friends to form an impromptu band and no one spotted the difference.

Whilst on the subject of robberies, I recall the police raid on Castle Bromwich Hall to seek "trophies" obtained from a hop at the Studley Agricultural College. On entering Peter Lockton's room they observed a bed-side light constructed from a blue police sign recently obtained by Brian Bruce (it was alleged) from a parked police car outside Steel House Lane police station.

My apprenticeship was nearly concluded for the first time after two days. I commenced on the 6th September 1954 in the Cost Office run by George Huddlestone who was off sick for my period of 3 months, so I was placed under the supervision of John Sturrock who took delight in setting me up, especially when I was sent on an errand to see Mr. Funnifoot. This character, in charge of publicity brochures, lived in the basement of the Administration block, and as I discovered to my embarrassment, his name was Sillitoe.

Next door to the Cost Office was the Accounts run by Alf Harper. Alf always had a tipped cigarette in his mouth and bets were placed as to the time when the ash would fall off. He never exercised those facial muscles which enable homo-sapiens to smile; if he did it would probably have dislodged his cigarette. Now Alf was in charge of the Sunstrand girls, one of whom I was very attracted to. She had the most magnificent frontage and I spent much time at her side watching it all tremble in harmonic motion each time the carriage of her accounting machine hit a tab stop. On the 7th of September, Alf put the fear of God in me and threatened to sack me if I ever set foot in there again. I did, however, manage to take her to dance at the Hall but, regrettably nothing developed further.

The second occasion of early threatened dismissal centred around the Jazz Band Ball held at the Magnet Club. The regulation 400 tickets were put on sale and quickly sold out; a rare success for any Ape Do. I recalled earlier organising a dance at the West End Ballroom under the baton of Sonny Rose and only sold 3 tickets 2 days before the event. So armed with this opportunity for a major contribution to funds, I sallied forth to Lewis's and purchased a John Bull printing outfit so tickets could be made available on demand. (I still think Arnold Weinstock would have been proud of me).

The scene changes to the night of the Ball. By 8.15 the draught beer had run out, by 8.45 the bottle beer had been drunk, and by 9.15 washroom porcelain was being dismembered. Over 720 had attended. Fire regulations permitted 400.

The following Monday morning I was summonsed to Rollason's office, I had taken the precaution of warning my landlady on Sunday evening that my departure may be imminent, and could I be relieved of the fortnight's notice.

Rollason: Did you know about the state of the Magnet Club on Saturday night?

Me: Yes, sir.

Rollason: How many tickets did you have printed?

Me: 400 sir, (quickly offering the printer's invoice)

Rollason: There were more than 400 there

Me: Were there?

Rollason: How much money did you make?

Me: (Proudly) £53 sir.

Rollason: (In total disbelief that the Apprentices had organised something that did not require a Company subsidy) You had better give Bill Corner £20 and don't break fire regulations again.

Me: Phew!

Another of John Sturrocks endearments was to set up his colleagues. One character in the Cost Office always put his head in his arms at lunch time and went to sleep. On one occasion, I was elected to change the office clock after lunch to 5.18 and persuade the rest of the office to pretend to be leaving as if it was the close of play for the day. It nearly went horribly wrong when I tapped the guy on the shoulder indicating it was time to go home. He went a deathly white thinking he had slept all through the afternoon session. It took him some time to recover, much to the mirth of the office.

A2.2 Dick Palmer, apprentice 1934-1938.

On arrival at Witton at the tender age of 16 years, I was introduced to the Apprentices Association by Nigel Holmes, but after a few days came into the sight of T.G.Smith and was told off for not appearing to be working in the Installation Department.

The most dramatic time during the years was when an apprentice (whose name I have forgotten) was electrocuted in Standard Test. He handled a synchronising 2 pole switch with both hands as the top wooden handle was missing. I was subpoenaed to attend the inquest, but was not called upon to give evidence. It was interesting to see that the switches were fitted with handles immediately after the accident

Later that year, 3 of us from Standard Test went with a number of apprentices from Austin to Germany to visit some of the factories, and also visit the Olympic Games, and was interested to see the games on a T/V set many miles away from Berlin. In all, we were away from Witton for 2 weeks , but the normal holiday period was only 1 week. Therefore Mr. Cape was most angry when 3 of his apprentices were missing as Mr. Cape had not been told that "Bogey" Heaton, the Works Manager, had given his approval to the German trip.

During the years I was secretary of the AA (*Apprentices ass.*) and so had a key to the special office in the roof of the Main Shop, where many an hour was spent producing Apprentice's Journal of which I was for some time the editor.

I did not fancy working on "nights" in Transformer Test, but was at last forced to go. However, after only one week I was transferred to Rotating Plant Design Office for the rest of my apprenticeship, and remained in that department for the rest of my stay in Witton until I was made redundant in 1979.

I made many friends during my apprenticeship, some of whom have now passed away.

A2.3 R. W. Sunley apprentice, GEC Witton, 1955-1960

Having never been back to Birmingham since 1960, the Apes reunion dinner was a really fantastic and emotional experience, and something I regret not doing more often. I hope there will be further opportunities. Here are a few odd memories as they come;

Castle Bromwich Hall figured high in my memories. My first meeting with Rollason was to complain that my weeks wages were £2-4 shillings, and my Hall bill was £2-14. What was to be done? This compared with an earlier big meeting with Rollason and several other speakers to an audience of several hundred including 300 apprentices, where salaries of £1000 were suggested inside one year!!

I remember the Hall party committee and the disappearing "ideas" man. Also, Peter Lockton's cry of "Bus up!" at an unearthly hour in the morning, and also his general leadership. There was the night the Council left a steam-roller in the Hall yard, Gardner(?) got it fired up and rolling towards the Hall and didn't know how to stop it!! One night an ass was brought into the yard and tethered next to the dustbins. At an early hour came an amazing noise of "braying" followed by clashing dustbins. A major enquiry followed.

The winters must have been colder, much colder in the 50's. David Lloyd drove his car on to, and eventually off the ice on the Sutton Park lakes, and I can remember buying my own skates and skating on various ponds and lakes with Roger Hockin(?) and others on more than one winter

At Witton itself, to a country boy the whole thing was a source of wonder, "clocking in" was a whole new experience. Tea breaks again were an unknown experience, and then the numbers of people! I suppose *circa* 10k would be employed in those high days. There didn't seem to be much protection against fumes and dust; in the mica shop and the open plating vats in switchgear, I can never remember wearing a hat, goggles, or breathing apparatus.

We had some major visits which we had to host, including the I.E.E and the Russian leader, was in Malenkov? and we had to plan these with precision. I soon moved to Outside Erection where there were any number of characters. I once dated Catherine Jukes, whose Dad turned out to be the senior man in one of the Groups (*and eventually Head of all Outside staff, and a very important man).* Then there was George Brand, the Evans twins, and Dai "bach" Evans, all veterans of the middle East and various steel works jobs including R.T.B. Llanwern and John Summers. One big learner was a Malaysian Engineer, and Dai "bach" had, in the spare moments between shut downs, taught him the Welsh words to "Sospan Bach" the Welsh anthem. Then taken into the local pubs, and bets taken, the rendering was word perfect!

Time runs out, to finish with a tale of J.J.Gracie (*the works general manager).* He made friends with a man on a cruise on the Queen Mary who persuaded J.J. to take his less than talented son on as an apprentice. The lad with thick glasses and no obvious abilities at anything, struggled to survive. His main achievement was in avoiding work in the factory by staying in the toilets, and his only claim to fame was once falling asleep and being locked in the factory after work.

A2.4 Bill Bennet, Switchgear Works, 1950-1969

Many thanks for your invitation, and sorry for the delay in replying. I enjoyed your anecdotes and tales of "Witton".

I recall many amusing incidents at Witton in my time there. One particular one concerns No2 Drawing Office. The toilets there were built of glazed brick and because of poor tolerances each wooden (lift off) door was individually made. One evening, during overtime we lifted all these doors off and stacked them at the end with a notice pinned on "Please take one" The next morning with at least 12 out of approx. 200 draughtsmen in dire straits, their comments need not be described. I believe to this day some of those doors do not fit properly!

I recall a welder in H.T.Fabrication shop who used to have a nap in his lunch time having the steel tips of his boots tack welded to the bench! Nails through enamel tea mugs were commonplace. I have the photo of you at the Xmas dinner in the skiffle group with the two managers and others!

Hope the foregoing is of some interest.

P.S. When Witton closed in 1969 I had served 19 years and 6 months. It was the practice to give a gold watch after 20 years service. I felt aggrieved by this at being forced out so I made an appointment with Mr. Muret (*then the Manager*) to plead for my watch. He was sympathetic, but unable to agree, so I then suggested I would accept it minus the strap! His face was a picture, but no luck. A few days later through the internal post came a battered old TIMEX watch with no hands, all neatly parcelled up. I could write pages of similar incidents.

A2.5 Maurice James Apprentice, 1959-1963

Sorry I have not replied earlier, but I very much appreciate the project you have undertaken.

One of my early memories was of the "ladies" in W.M.I. (*Witton Moulded Insulations*). After the Machine School I had a job in Electricians Section. We went to repair a fault in W.M.I. and I carried the ladder. When we arrived I rested it on the overhead pipes, and the bang on the pipes had the effect of releasing some very black dirt from overhead. The "ladies" expressed their disapproval in language I had not heard from men in my sheltered youth .I wondered if I would get out alive, but somehow managed to escape.

I also remember in my early days an apprentice falling asleep in turbo test and pressing the big red stop button halfway through a heat run. Getting back to the same condition took many hours.

At Castle Bromwich Hall we had regular fire practice and I had a very memorable incident. I was a "dummy" in an evacuation exercise via the third floor window. I was carried out on a shoulder but my feet were left in. I finished up sliding down the fireman's back into a handstand on the ladder. You can imagine what it was like from that height and the struggle to recover. Somehow I made it without injury, watched by a white-faced Peter Lockton.

Site work at the Ebbw Vale steel works was also interesting. Builders took a short cut through a sub-station and rubbed a scaffolding pole on the bus-bar. Fortunately, the carrier was on a rubber mat, but the fireworks started when the other end touched the metal ground. Permanent notches were left in the bus-bars. I also remember doing an insulation test on the High Voltage motors. After the test I nipped up the ladder to take off the leads; nobody had told me about the static charge! When I grabbed the leads, I thought somebody had turned on the 11kV. All good experience.

I have many other fond memories of the Witton days, but these are the ones which stand out most. Thanks for all your efforts, and best wishes.

A2.6 Dereck Davies, Apprentice, and part-owner of the famous "bomb". Witton, 1950–1954

Sorry not to have written sooner, but memory recall is not so good these days! There are a couple of stories which might be of interest, the first about the "Bomb" and the second about an infamous lady in Standard Motor winders.

The Bomb was a 1925, 12.5 HP London taxi jointly owned by Bob Beard (Australia), Lou Green (Argentine) and Doug Cunliffe (Australia) and yours truly. There were several incidents which I recall;

For one of the Apes performances at the Annual Dinner I was charged with obtaining various costumes including a polar bear outfit. The play, I think, was Sudav Ouq written by Ken Parton and Peter Barton. Rollason was played by Ian Stewart (who else!), and Ron Getwood played Hudson (Soapy). One of the scenes was selling ice cream to Eskimos, hence the polar bear outfit.

Transport to collect the costumes was the bomb. To digress a little, one needs to know that on the back of the bomb was painted the words "Don't laugh, your daughter may be inside". The driver's door had dotted lines with the words "To open, tear along the dotted line". The *Piece de resistance* was the coat of arms. Within the outline of a shield were painted a crossed hammer and chisel and below the shield were the outline of what were then naughty words "IFCI—WF" which to many nurses and other sensitive souls meant "If we can't fix it—we're finished" to less sensitive mortals, the last word was changed.

Several of us were delegated to collect the costumes from Barnham's in Birmingham using the bomb. Again to digress slightly, a 1925 London taxi did not have the equivalent of anti-locking brakes or for that matter hydraulic assisted breaking—it was brute force on the pedals but mainly relying on the hand brake. Approaching an island in the centre of Birmingham the brakes failed—a cable fault! And we needed to stop. The only solution which immediately came to mind was to go round the island several times gradually slowing down by rubbing the tyres against the curb. This had the effect of slowing us down helped by two passengers jumping out and trying physically to stop the bomb by putting chocks under the wheels, (a very high risk exercise). The costumes were duly collected, having effected a temporary repair (at all times we carried an extensive tool kit, a most important item being Bostik).

In returning to Witton, we came along the No. 11 bus route towards Perry Bar. Along that route the road forked to the left near a cinema whose entrance was approached by quite an extensive sweep of stone steps. The reason for mentioning the No.11 bus route is pertinent in as much as a bus stop was situated directly in front of the stone steps, but by some quirk the bus stop to the buses in the opposite direction was situated such that with two buses each stopped at the bus stops it was not possible to get between them. To add to the problem, the left fork had a slight downward slope. In applying the brakes with some caution it became obvious the bomb would not stop. The only option was to mount the curb, and make our way up the steps of the cinema, by-pass the bus and in doing so causing some consternation with the queue of people waiting for the Saturday morning show!

It was custom and practice that whenever the bomb was on tour we would not only give lifts to lady hitch-hikers but also to lady cyclists. The roof rack would take comfortably 3 cycles and of course there was ample room inside for a happy exchange of conversation. We did install a switchboard indicating light which was flashed on and off by the driver if the conversation became secondary to other activities. The driver's position was quite independent of the passengers with only a luggage space by his side. In one case we did install a spare seat with ropes to prevent the re-occurrence of an episode when the passenger in the luggage space fell asleep and toppled out on to the road. Fortunately it was when taking a sharp bend at 5 mph. 30mph. was maximum speed.

Driving through Warrington on a return trip to Witton, I was driving with "L" plates on display and Bob Beard was the competent driver supervising me. Bob was otherwise engaged, having had several flashes of the indicating light when a police siren sounded behind us, We could not be speeding, even if we wanted to, and I was driving very cautiously because of our brakes. In fact, every time we were overtaken we had to reduce speed to ensure we always had sufficient stopping distance from the vehicle in front.

The police, no doubt curious with the various writings on the bomb, stopped us and asked to see my licence, which was a learner's licence. Having satisfied himself the papers were in order, he asked if the bomb was road worthy and in particular, were the brakes in order. To drive the bomb was not easy, it was a crash gear box, with the need to double de-clutch each time the gear was changed. The only way out was to be bold and so we invited the policeman to drive the bomb and see for himself. Fortunately, he declined the offer, but charged me with breaking the law because the competent driver was not sitting adjacent to me. Despite the fact we said it was not possible, I was duly summonsed to attend court in Warrington.

Employing legal representation in those days was out of the question, but the next best thing was to speak to CID Syd, the works inspector of police. (*At Witton*) A suitable letter was drafted which I found difficult to follow, which said in effect there was no such offence in the statute book. I never even received an acknowledgement to the letter and I never did go to Warrington again.

In the years 50-54, the bomb was a common sight on the Witton estate. We had special permission to service the Bomb in the Turbo Shop, and we have to thank Dunlop who provided the special tyres. We were able to keep the Bomb in service until about 1954 when

Bob Beard left and I went into the army. However, Bob actually drove the Bomb to the scrap yard. The Bomb was probably well known by the nurses at Woodlands Hospital when we transplanted as many as 12 at a time between the Magnet Club and Woodlands!

Having given further consideration to my second story I think it best to leave it untold except to say there are many of us who, when working in SM winders, were taught there was more to life than winding stators. The mere mention of SM winders will, I am sure, bring a smile to the lips of many an apprentice, especially Pete Hipwell and Nigel Steeley.

P.S. I have a considerable number of photographs, in fact the master copies of the Sidav Ouq show, including the whole assembly at the Magnet Club. Would this be of interest?

Sorry again to have been so long; I have also just retired!

A2.7 Peter Bishop "Memories of Witton" 1957–1960

As a commercial apprentice with GEC at Witton (1957-60) my memories are not so much about Main Test and the shop floor, but about the offices and the administration which oiled the wheels and kept the score of the electrical engineering exploits.

My first memories are of the Accounts Dept and the Cost Office in the main administration block on the ground floor. What an impressive building! Accounts and Cost office were run on Dickensian protocols, we didn't exactly sit on stools but the chairs were hard, upright and unadjustable. Being short, I "acquired" a small box on which to rest my feet! mine was very basic, but some footstools were more elaborate. The whole atmosphere was gloomy and formal due to being flanked on either side by other tall buildings, small window panes covered in Witton discharges of many years, and the economics demonstrated by strict control of the lighting. Filing cabinets around sections and high piles of paper on desks further constricted the flow of light.

The characters, mostly names forgotten now, are the memorable parts. The lady who ran the Sale and Bought ledger section who sat on a particularly high chair by the window, encapsulated by lever arch box files. If one summonsed up the courage to approach her to ask a question it felt like going into a concentration camp! I remember being amazed at the affairs that went on in the office (mostly all talk) and in particular the way the older men chatted up the juniors. One of the high spots in any week was when Tennant (the chief accountant) had a major query or panic and the whole office erupted into major activity, everyone seemed to be drawn in to help whether they had a real contribution to make or not. I remember the celebrations with cakes on birthdays, births, marriages etc; watching the clerks fall asleep after lunch and noting the ingenuity with which they covered up their slumbers—the big old journal ledgers could prop up a 12 stone man for hours!

We also got involved with other departments. I remember the buyer who re-furbished a cottage in Wales from parts and supplies "acquired" variously from Witton. I remember the tunnel between the main Administration block and Switchgear—well decked in graffiti and a perilous place to pass through as a young male about Christmas time because of the "girls" who lay in wait!

The really memorable events that linger, however, are more related to outside work activities. Life at Castle Bromwich Hall is still a vivid memory as the following illustrate:-

-the wonderful parties when the Hall was decorated, plays were performed by the apprentices, usually under the direction of Peter Barton. The activities around the Hall and in the maze and gardens would form the plot of many a best seller.

-the myriads of old motorbikes and cars which the apprentices worked on in the old stables and out-buildings of the Hall, mostly they were worked on without completion being achieved. One fun activity was to remove the underpants of those stripped off and washing the oil and grease off their hands after being immersed in their mechanical hobby. A great chase and pillow fight usually ensued.

-one evening, one of the more renowned "amorous" students at the Hall had dressed up in a new white shirt and light grey trousers before dinner, all ready for a quick exit for the "date" which was planned. We had fish and chips with the usual display of large HP Tomato Ketchup bottles on the table. I was always accustomed to giving the sauce bottle a good shake before using it to make the sauce of more even consistency. Unfortunately, the lid had not been screwed on. Yes, you have guessed! I shook the bottle vigorously and tomato sauce shot all over our amorous colleague. The air was blue and I still have the scars. Fish and chips with tomato sauce have never tasted the same since.

-fire practice and drill was a weekly event, the fire alarm usually went off early on Sunday morning when most of us wished to sleep still in recovery of the Saturday night out. Being the smallest member of the fire team, it was sometimes my lot to be carried up and down the ladders, feigning fainting from smoke fumes.

-being in one of the front bedrooms at the Hall was a distinct disadvantage, the door of the Hall was shut around 11 pm. I recall. Whilst there was a fire escape, most late-comers preferred to throw gravel up at the bedroom windows to wake the occupants to come down and let them in. Friendships were variously lost and gained in the process.

-one of the great pastimes from the Hall was to go out on parties on what would now be termed "vandalism" rounds. I remember a number of English Electric transformers on low loaders were given a very decorative exterior with streamers, bunting, etc. The local colleges also received our attention from time to time. Basically it was in high spirits with no damage being done.

-sport was a big element of apprentice's life. Rugby and hockey were those indulged in my time. GEC had its own apprentices teams, we were even coached by Peter Jackson of England fame. The annual trip to Twickenham (as spectators, not players) was a highlight of the season—but probably not for the coach driver!

-the Operatic and Dramatic society (OADS) was another activity which apprentices got involved in- as actors, singers, stage management and building sets. A very lively time was enjoyed and plays were also a feature of parties at the Hall. The "foreigners" which were mysteriously produced as props, scenery, etc. were a credit both to the ingenuity of the apprentices and to the resources at Witton. On one occasion, I remember a toilet seat was cast in the foundry for one sketch that was performed.

Yes, they were memorable, exhiliarating and formative days.

A2.8 Gina Dodd, Witton, (1944–1948)

(Miss Dodd was one of only three female apprentices. One of the others was Margaret Weston, who left to soon become Manager of the Science Museum in London, a post she held with distinction until she retired)

When I applied to Witton in the hope of becoming a student apprentice, T.G.Smith was in the process of handing over the job of keeping us in order, to an individual by the name of Seaman. The reply to my letter was addressed to *Miss E.G.Dodd Esq* and post-marked the day *before* the date of the letter. It did however offer me an interview and along I trotted on the appointed day. Seamen was housed in a diminutive office near the main Time Lodge and the porch, if I remember correctly housed two doorways at right angles to each other but at 45 degrees to the roadway. Did the Safety Officer at the time inhabit the twin office?

When anyone knocked on the door the secretary's face appeared through a chink in the doorway, then if she decided to admit you, she re-closed the door, climbed behind her own desk, and opened the door wide enough for you to enter. No wonder she was soon christened "Little Bo-Peep" in the Apprentices Journal! As Betty Barwell and Margaret Weston were already on the premises the Management must have decided to submit to the changing times with good grace because I got no dissuasive lecture, and a starting date was agreed provided I could get the necessary Labour Exchange documentation in time. And that was where the fun started.

At the Wolverhampton Labour Exchange the girl behind the counter took ages to fill in the first few lines of a form then, when she discovered I had School Certificate (*O level*) Maths and Physics, she declared I was in the wrong place and should go to the Technical Service Register, buried in some back street dive. There I was given the same form to fill in myself. I preened myself on the improved status of my chosen career. The satisfaction was short lived: the conversation went something like this;-

Counter Clerk: "OK we'll let you know"

Me:"Let me know what?"

C.C,"Let you know when we've found you a suitable job"

Me:"But I've already got a job, I'm going to be an Electrical Engineer"

C.C, enraged: "You can't go around finding your own job. There's a *war* on. You've got to do something *useful!*"

We compromised by my taking the documents and agreeing to go back if they ever sent for me, which of course never happened

The things which stick in my mind from this time include:

The area eventually occupied by the new big shop was indeed a car park with the Labour Office (no one having heard of Personnel) housed in a wooden shack at the Main Gate. From there was handed over a Work's Pass, with dire warnings of the consequences of losing it. Actually I was never once asked to show it, but what was much more valuable was the under-21's Cocoa Ticket which entitled the bearer to a fairly palatable alternative to Work's tea in the morning.

Government Shop: Embroidery silk had disappeared from the shops early in the war, but here it was in a range of lovely colours being used to secure the insulation wrapping on coils before they were dipped. The stuff was so pinchable that it was kept strictly under lock and key and immediately a skein came to light it was cut into lengths too short to be threaded into a needle—I could have wept. Later on in the test section the foreman knew he was right in blaming me for the magnet trademark painted on the knife handle because "his girls always drew the coils wrongly"

Mica Shop: Joe Binks must surely have been in his late 70's? He was reputed to have only joined Witton on retiring from a proper job. He seemed to take one tour of his 3 storey domain, by lift, each day and then sit ruminating at his desk.

Switchgear Works: On the oil switch section my mate was just completing the assembly of a bunch of 8 oil switches. He seemed to be running short of components and kept sending me to a huge wooden box under the bench to find 6 of this or 10 of that for each switch. As the box contained every size of screw from about 6BA to

3/8 Whitworth, in a wide range of lengths and heads with nuts and washes ditto, it became a bit tedious.

Then came the great day when there was a new order started. I was given the job of writing the requisitions for just about everything on the drawings. I delightedly fetched a positive truck load of components from the stores, all in neat little brown paper packets suitably labelled with stock numbers etc., and looked forward to a more constructive use of my time, but not a bit of it. To my horror my mate counted off the packages then ripped them all open and tossed the contents into his stock pot!

Fan Assembly: The general advice handed down from generation to generation of apprentices was "never discuss politics or religion in the shops; it will only get you into trouble." Imagine my surprise, therefore, to find that a gang of men in this department subscribed to Hansard and held regular lunch time discussions on its contents.

At the other extreme, the girl on the tea trolley in this shop was, to put it mildly, not much to look at. She was always talking about winning a beauty competition, which took a bit of believing, but it turned out that her boyfriend was a photographer and she did indeed look good on paper.

S M Winders: They were just changing over from winding armatures of Admiralty blowers to winding stators for loom motors. The planning department had decided to abandon the long work benches and instead equip the shop with individual work stations. A sample table was made up and each of the girls was put to work for a week and then asked for their comments. Now this was always done with Weaver Senior standing by and he was such a tartar that nobody would venture to express an opinion in front of him. In desperation the charge hand put me on to it.

It was an incredible contraption. There was an angle iron piece under the front edge of the table which left no room for the slimmest legs between it and a standard GEC stool. Then the tool tray was not quite wide enough so whatever you needed always had to be grovelled for. Most startling of all, the thing had a swivelling top so that it was easy to turn the work piece round and tackle either end of the job; the problem was that it was a square work bench and the swivelling member was also

242 TALES FROM THE TOOLBOX

square, hence the poor operator got a smart dig in the ribs umpteen times
a day. Like a lamb to the slaughter I told the planner what I thought of all
this and was hauled up before Weaver to repeat the accusations. He was so
furious that I concluded that he had designed it himself!

The sequel, many months later, was that Weaver caught me near
the Time Lodge at home time one evening and asked me to go and
look at the top winders shop, above the old big shop winding bay. On
the way up in the lift he gave me a lecture on the error of my ways in
"so despising that stator winding station." He said that not only was
SM now full of them but he was about to show me a shop filled with
a larger version of the same thing.

It was true, but I noticed that the bigger version included all my
suggested improvements. He was such a funny cuss, I don't know to
this day whether that was the nearest he could get to an apology. I
think it was more likely that he had persuaded himself they were
entirely his own design. Fortunately, I was anxious to get home early
that night so for once I my life I had the sense to keep my mouth shut.

1947: Life suddenly got a bit more serious with the big freeze up
and the fuel crisis, and even though we were indentured apprentices,
we were "given the sack", though in the event the Works re-opened
for business before the seven days notice expired.

It was certainly a great place to receive ones training though what
you learned in my day was more by absorption than formal
indoctrination. The spirit of the place must have been something very
special for it not only survived the later ravages of time and Big
Business, it seemed to positively strengthen from 1958 onwards. To
jump forward to 1966 when I was sold to C.A.Parsons and spent time
almost commuting back from Witton to Newcastle, I became very
conscious of the value of this. On my return trips I was made equally
welcome in the Big Shop and in the works managers office. The only
difference was that the slinger on the big crane would put the current
day's Daily Mirror on his tool box for me to sit on whereas Peter
Lockton would throw the previous day's Financial Times at me to use
as protection for his carpets from my oily shoes.

I felt the Witton Spirit was present in full force on the night of the
Dinner—how privileged we all are to have experienced it.

A2.9 Arthur Davies 1936-1940, and Design Office afterwards

Following upon a letter that I have received from David Rawcliffe, I enclose a few stories of my early days at Witton as an apprentice and in design office afterwards. I trust that they will be worthy of inclusion in your collection.—- Wishing you all the best in your coming retirement, you will find that there will be insufficient time when it comes to do all you think you will do when you no longer have to travel each day

I commenced my apprenticeship in the electrician department in 1936, and I well remember one apprentice who kept chasing the foreman, Ted Ferris, for work. In the end Ted said to Bob Ashfield, the electrician with whom I was working, "I'll stop the b———r!" and the next time the silly "Ape" asked for more work gave him a length of 6" dia. steel bar and told him to hacksaw two 1" lengths off it. The message was not lost on him, no more requests for work.

One day in May whilst working in the commutator section in "A" shop, which was above the main stores that ran between the main and standard fitting shops, the works Manager, known as Bogey Heaton, walked down the small assembly shop and noticed rubbish and dirt between two benches. Picking up a broom which was nearby he swept between the two benches, put the broom down and walked off. Half an hour later he re-appeared – no sign of rubbish anywhere only a very red-faced foreman.

During the early days of the war when the blitz appeared to be about to commence, we had a Chinese apprentice named Tommy Koh on nights with us. Tommy was the only member of the shift without a tin hat so a civilian type of helmet was left for him by the shift foreman. Tommy was delighted, and insisted that it be tested. He asked a tester to stand on a table and hit him with a piece of 3" square wood about 2 ft. long. After we had picked him up, still groggy, he was most upset because of the large dent in the top of the helmet and not worried about the headache he suffered for the rest of the night shift.

At the beginning of the blitz we were (3 Testers) on nights in rectifier division (MAR) and during an air raid there was a shower of incendiary bombs dropped all around the building, not one actually hitting it. On going outside one was seen to be burning merrily inside the main transformer pen, so grabbing buckets of sand we three tried to smother the fire. By this time Mr. E. Gallizia, the manager of M.A.R. dashed out and on his knees alongside the bomb, using only his hands, piled the sand up higher. The transformer was saved, but the headlines the next morning said "Explosive incendiary bombs dropped all over Birmingham last night". He was exceedingly pale and quiet all the next day at the thought of what might have happened.

Another war time memory:— I was working in the laboratory using a small Mercury Arc Rectifier as an electronically controlled switch to drive a Pom-Pom Gun that was mounted at the end of one of the bays of the laboratory. The supplies to the gun went normally via a great many slip rings underneath, via a total of 2 miles of cable. For experimental purposes the cables were connected directly to the internal connections, hence a limited rotation of 2 turns of the gun in each direction was possible. Mr. H.V. Alexander, First Lord of the Admiralty, was coming to see the demonstration and Dr. Wilson was intent on operating the gun from the platform joystick himself. He was advised against doing this but insisted and so was warned not to move more than 2 rotations in either direction. Come the day, H.V. Alexander and Doc Wilson got on the gun, round two turns, then reverse. Whilst going back in the reverse direction he discovered he could raise the gun barrels at the same time with the same joystick; so, carried away with this discovery he forgot to count the number of rotations. Result two miles of cable completely ripped from the gun!

A2.10 Bob South, Apprentice 1937-1941. Eventually in the Motor Design Office

In reply to your request I enclose a few stories which might be of interest covering 1937-1941. The more one writes, the more the memories come flooding back but one has to draw the line somewhere. Like many others I would dearly love to have a tape of Peter's (Armitage) wonderful speech. I wish you every success with this venture, and a well-earned retirement in August.

A review of the pre-war apprentices financial lot might be worth recording. The lucky applicant, having successfully survived the Bogey Heaton/ T.G.Smith interview could not be accepted until father had deposited £50 to ensure that the Company would be compensated to a small degree for any damage his son might produce. I'm sure this amount was exceeded on many occasions. Pay started at 8/6d per week (*about 30p*) for the first year, less insurance, which resulted in 7/2½d in one's pay packet. Afterwards the amount was increased by 1/- per week at 6 monthly intervals, finishing with the worldly sum of 14/6d. It was a great event to find a crisp 10/- (*50p*) note in one's pay packet.

Payment was made on Friday nights (after the bell) had gone from a wooden pay box mounted on cast-iron wheels—akin to a Victorian bathing hut situated outside the Time Lodge. The Apes had to queue until all the electricians had been paid. Demonstrations against the wait frequently resulted in a scrum forming behind the box which was propelled across the road into the Carbon Works with the poor terrified female wages clerk inside. Opposition from the Works police had no chance. Pay was confiscated which meant a visit to Wages Dept. at midday on Saturday where the confusion was even greater. Eventually we did get our own pay box.

While working in the Electrician's Dept. in early 1938 I was involved with the installation of the induction regulators in Main Test. Fixing up the bus-bar system around the walls of the test involved one being in perilous situations on crane rails with an aerial view of the activities of more senior Apes working below, surrounded by bare copper wires and instruments, testing large machines with experiments resulting in large flashes and bangs. I was convinced at the time that I would be very lucky if I completed my apprenticeship alive.

Subsequently I well remember Peter Troupe excelling himself by shorting out the 460 volt bus-bar system round the test, bombarding those at ground level with broken porcelain egg insulators. For his sins he was relegated to the Instrument Room where he could do less damage. Whether the accuracy of his meter calibrations could be trusted was never known.

In my early days in the Electricians, "tear-arse" Ted Ferris came into the Dump and said "Come with me son" so I dutifully followed him at the trot, a pace behind. We journeyed at a high rate of knots around the Estate, through Standard, Engineering, Switch and Transformer, he looking at various wiring jobs. He suddenly stopped, turned to me and looked at me—"What do you keep following me for son, what do you want?" "You told me to come with you" "I don't want you for anything, you'd better go back and find your mate" The reason for his request has remained a mystery.

The pre-war Annual dinners were a mixture of formal and informal affairs, the informal part resulting from the show which was a series of crude skits on Witton notables coupled with the usual smutty black-out sketches, the audience being well jugged up on the best Magnet Club mild.—nothing to be compared with the magnificent productions of the later Parton/Barton period. I recall a speech at one dinner by the late Bill Bird who had attained giddy heights in the company since his apprenticeship, becoming Sales Director at Magnet House, Kingsway. He started as a shy young apprentice working his way up through various commercial departments until he reached the stage where he could talk to Miss Dolly Howard as man to man!

The setting up of Scrounge holes was an important part of one's working life, and dodging or leading the Works Police up the garden path was a good pastime. The Works Police under Hope— CID Sid was not around at that time—were supported by under-cover men, generally toilet cleaners, "Sh—house Alfie", brother of Mrs. Mason the Welfare Officer being the most notorious. The most outstanding experts in subterfuge were David and Frank Evans, identical twins, who foxed police and shop management alike, some not even being aware there were two of them. While one took time off the other would double for his brother, appearing in both departments on and off and even getting involved in each other's work. One would allow himself to be followed by the police, allowing the other to gain access to a scrounge hole undetected. The decoy would then return to his place of work leaving his follower confused. The best scrounge hole was provided by the Company, exclusively to committee members who had access to a strange box-like office mounted above the fitting bay in the old engineering shop. We even had a 'phone installed.

Time keeping was always a problem and getting to the clocks in the Time Lodge was always a mad rush before the gates were closed. Apes' time cards not clocked in were removed and sent to T.G.Smith so that the poor unfortunate could be disciplined. During my period as Social Secretary my clock card never reached T.G.Smith. I used to employ Jesse Taylor, a decent member of the pollce who worked in the Time Lodge and as door-keeper at apprentice's functions, when he did well with tips and drinks.

Just after the end of my apprenticeship, I was summonsed with others to Miss Howard's office and we were ushered into J.J.G's office (*Managing director*) —one at a time—to be interviewed by senior members of the 3 services and a white-haired professor of law. It appeared that they had heard of the splendid apprenticeship scheme at GEC and gave us the choice of accepting a technical commission in the Services of one's choice or staying on in industry for the duration of the war. J.J.G tried to put a spanner in the works by saying how useful one was to the company, but to no avail.

In a few weeks I started another apprenticeship—learning to be an RAF Electrical Engineering Officer. I subsequently found how valuable my GEC training had been, not just the technical aspects but the understanding of people, and acceptance of responsibility and improvisation, being responsible for the technical ability and the welfare of the troops under one's command.

A2.11 Stuart (Ray) Judd , Mercury-arc rectifier works (MAR) 1945-1952

Last week, I received David's Rawcliffe's letter asking for Witton anecdotes etc. to be sent to you. I hope that the attached will be of use. I have had to compile them rather hurriedly as Marguerite and I are on holiday in a couple of weeks and I know you want copy by mid-July. Thanks for offering to do all the copying, I look forward to seeing the final result.

I must say that I did not serve my apprenticeship with GEC, so my contribution may not be eligible in your 'opus, but I did have many very happy years with Sam Dale and his team in Rectifier Works,

Witton from 1945 until I transferred to Witton-James, Hendon London in 1952. David tells me that you will be retiring in August. I wish you well in your "third age". In September I shall have been retired for 11 years. Marguerite and I have no difficulty in filling our time with various activities and enjoying North Bedfordshire village life. Best Wishes.

Some off-the cuff memories;-

1. The wall poster behind Enrico Gallizia's (EG) desk which exhorted us to " a) Get the facts b) Weigh and decide c) Take action."

2. The pencil which EG flung across his table when a meeting was not going well

3. The gentle knock on the door during a meeting, EG saying "Come in" and Jim Benson quietly entering to ask if he could be allowed to leave because his house was on fire

4. EG running around MAR holding a smoking rag to check the effectiveness of the cooling system of his latest "Baby"

5. Ensuring that on Monday mornings there was enough space in our tiny Electronics Section to accommodate all the bits and pieces which Sam Dale brought in after a weekend in Shrewsbury, or elsewhere. These could be a cap, goggles, leggings, a huge waterproof mac, engine parts when he was motorcycling, exotic feathers for making fishing flies, fishing tackle, wood for violin making, cameras, underdeveloped films and watches etc., for the necessary attention.

6. Over the years Sam Dale had a variety of motorcycles and cars, but he was particularly proud of his Alvis. On one occasion its silencer failed. For once Sam's resourcefulness let him down, for the noise could be heard in MAR long after he had passed through the gates on the other side of the estate—despite the flue brush stuffed up the exhaust pipe.

7.Due to space limitations our work on the initial experimental electronically controlled motor equipment had to be done in a small corner of MAR Test, alongside the large motor-generator sets and immediately below the gallery on which short-circuit tests on high speed HV.DC air-break breakers were often done. Interrupting the fault current produced an exceedingly loud explosive sound. For safety reasons a single whistle blast was used to signal the onset of a test and two blasts for the completion. Sometimes the automatic sequence failed, there was no loud bang after the first whistle sound, and I and others were left mentally in the air.

8.Although EG, Dr. Thompson, and Ken Birks had organised MAR so that it could continue to function efficiently if they were elsewhere, this did not apply to the one secretary, or the one driver who fetched essential materials from the many "external" stores, nor to the one crane driver until a stand-in could be found.

9.Sam Dale had many favourite expressions. To those who worked closely with him "Going over the other side" could mean several things: visiting Humphrey Ward, John Gibson, Skipper Emms Dr. Friedlander, (these names conjure up unforgettable personalities) or: doing some important work in the dark room!

10.Devising a dictation technique to overcome the tedium of lengthy reports and instruction books by the use of a now old-fashioned tape recorder without the any ear-piece or other modern attachments. This meant the play-back was only through the loud-speaker in the typists office, only separated from WGT's (*Manager of the adjacent Development Laboratories*) office by a thin glass/steel partition. One day as I passed WGT's open door, he called me in, asking "Who is that talking next door?" When I explained that it was me on tape, he gave a sigh of relief saying "Thank goodness, I thought there were two of you"

11.The MARLAB Social Club was a wonderful innovation for it brought together two groups of most interesting and friendly people.

Marguerette and I have very pleasant memories of theatre and coach outings and the children's parties with "Uncle Henry" (*EG*) distributing the presents

12.Did the young people in George Davies's Youth Club ever get to see the many comics that appeared in the "in" tray on his desk, which made such interesting reading whilst waiting for him to turn up for a meeting?

13.lThe time when the river Thame over-flowed into Electric Avenue and the expression of frustration on the Estate Manager's face as he had to kick away the sand bags placed across the Main gate to protect the estate, because residents claimed that these were worsening the flooding in their houses.

14.In the 40/50's bicycles were in common use around the estate. I had visions that Dr. Wilson might do himself serious harm if ever he missed the saddle at the end of his gigantic leap; that Dr. Friedlander might fall off if he rode his "sit up" machine any slower; that ex-chief inspector Chibnell thought he was reviewing his troops as he rode majestically from one security gatehouse to another; that the full-time fireman who rode around the estate to inspect the fire-buckets might one day find sand or water underneath all the cigarette ends and waste paper!

15.Bob Hickling was the first person I met on the day I started at Witton. "What shall we call you?" he asked. "Take your pick" I replied telling him my two forenames. "Ray! Welcome to Witton" he said, and that abbreviation of my second name stayed with me throughout my career at MAR, Witton-James, and Hirst Research Centre. It was even adopted by customers at home and overseas, now it is just one more memory.

A2.12 D. McCliskie " Witton Days" 1949-1953 D.McCliskie

In response to your request for a story, and having searched the remainder of the brain, whilst painting the outside of the bungalow, I feel I can't do better than enlarge on my experience of one of Witton's most colourful characters: GERALD (JOE) HARRIES

Somewhere in the early 60,s, Joe joined us, from Witton, in the GEC Birmingham office, by then in Newhall street, and on one occasion I was conveying him from the clutches of Rupert Baron, along Victoria Road, Aston, when a careless motorist shot out of a side turning into our path. I braked hard and swerved around him, we both stopped, Joe's window came down, quick smart, and whilst I got into gear, ready for take-off, the offending driver received a Harries "broadside"- appertaining to his parentage, his inability to drive a nail and G.O.K. (G-*d only* knows) what other pleasantries-served up from beneath that black Homburg hat——I felt quite sorry for the chap.

A little later, whilst inculcating Joe into the manner of obtaining his expenses at the counter in the Accounts Dept., on the top floor of the "palace of varieties", somebody cracked a funny which prompted Joe to launch into one of his grade 1 laughs—complete with oscillating jaw and awe-inspiring guffaws!! The expressions of stark horror on the faces of several damsels present were fascinating.

How apt was Peter Armitage's description—"A bulldog licking piss off a nettle!"

Good luck with your efforts, and here's wishing you a truly happy retirement.

A2.13 David Rawcliffe, Recollections of GEC witton (Birmingham), apprentice 1947-1949

What a splendid idea. I had similar thoughts after the dinner and got as far as composing a letter to the IEE asking whether they were doing anything about putting on record some of the small-scale happenings on the shop floor and in the Drawing Ofices in the Electrical Industries before it is too late. I did not finish the letter and send it off but I might " get round tuit".

On a point of order, my version of Willie Wilson and his bicycle is that he always used to run alongside it then leap onto it from the side, and without putting a foot on the pedal. Perhaps the leap over the back wheel was an approved variant?

I like your story of JJ (J.J. Gracie, Works Manager) and his personal supervision of the Colliery Electric Winder contract. People outside the Industry would find it difficult to believe. Do you recall who invented the title of "Benevolent Bird of Prey" for dear old Skipper Emms? One thing we shall never see again is the massed start of the cyclists at 5.18 (quitting time) into Electric Avenue. Everything had to give way to them, cars, buses, lorries the lot.

I am enclosing 6 ½ pages of my recollections; please feel free to use them as you choose.

BACKGROUND. I started at Witton after 4 years in the RAF. Within days of my release from the Services in December 1946, I had applied to "undergo" a Graduate Apprenticeship and had been invited to apply for interview, bringing my School reports. Although I had been born in Birmingham and actually lived there from 1921 to 1943, yet I had never seen the sprawl of the jewel in the Railing crown. (*Sir Harry railing, chairman of the GEC group of Companies*) So I duly went there and met Rollie for the first time, and a few days later, received the Royal Assent. I began in the Bickford Road section of Witton Kramer with Michael Dudley who was ex-Navy. I sometimes wonder if we were the first ex-officers to go as Grad-Apes at Witton. Appropriately enough we were put to work on the sweeps for mine detectors.

It was here that we had our first lesson in the difference between the Services and Industry. About a quarter of an hour before knocking-off time we washed our hands and decided to make our way to the Magnet Club that we had been told about. A works copper materialised and politely asked where we were going; we told him and were advised "'ang on a bit son. It ain't time yet" So we hung on.

MAIN TEST. Everyone has a story about the night shift in Main Test. I was working with one of the incredible Staff Testers, ("incredible" because they had such a wide knowledge and experience of the bewildering range of decrepit-looking equipment in the test.) We had set up a load test on an ac. motor of 50-100 HP which was loaded onto one of the dc test plant machines, and I had been left to keep an eye on it while the Tester made a start on the paperwork. He had been gone about 10 minutes when the door of the Power Station opened and a guy sauntered in quietly. He glanced around and came up to me asking quietly "Are you feeding back dc.power?" A bit of quick thinking and I said "Yes, I suppose we are." At once he simply exploded "Well get the f—cking thig off. I can't get rid of dc at this time of night."

It never occurred to me at the time, but had I been set up?

I wish I could recall the name of one of the Testers who always used to do the traction motors. He had to carry out a load test at the end of which he used to start a stop-watch and shut down as quickly as he could and start measuring a series of armature and field resistances as the machine cooled down, so as to be able to plot graphs and extrapolate to find the peak temperatures. It was the fast shut down that was so exciting, as he had a string of about 8 knife switches which all had to be pulled out as part of the shut down and it looked like a comic relief ballet.

TEA MAKING. Some of the tales of Witton have been handed down so one cannot vouch for them. One of those that comes under the "Wicked Bosses" category dates back to the days when private brew-ups were prohibited. If one of the foreman patrolling his manor came across an illicit tea-can sitting on a gas ring all by itself, he would just stand and watch it boil until it went dry and burned a hole in the can. Then he would walk away. There was a notice on a wall which said "Any employee putting tea-leaves down this drain will be instantly dismissed"

ENRICO GALLIZIA (Manager of Rectifier Works). In the Lab and Rectifier Works he was always known as "EG". Although not very tall he was solidly built and was a good swimmer. The story goes that at some sort of fete there was a "Guess your weight" booth. The guesser (or should we say "Estimator") misjudged EG's weight badly. He estimated the weight about a stone less than it was.

The other EG story goes back to the days when steel-tank pumpless rectifiers were being developed in the lab. EG was in the work-shop when a labourer came in and said "I've got something here for some bugger called Gerlisher. Do you know 'im? EG told him where his office was and he himself took a shorter route so that he was sitting at his desk before the guy reached there. History does not relate how it ended.

SITE WORK. Here again, this must be a fruitful source of anecdotes. My favourite one concerns the installations in the new factories of the Steel Company of Wales. Some of the machinery was so extensive that an inter-comm. system was essential. The system used involved loud-speakers all over the area including the under-floor chambers where the control panels were installed. One evening Glen Evans and the well-known Chinese commissioning engineer (was he Chen pao Chung?) were lying on the floor, no tables then, pouring over the drawings and discussing one of the many control problems which plague the lives on people on site. Every few minutes the intercom would squawk with incomprehensible noises in a strong South Wales voice as the two mechanical men toiled over their problems.

Finally, Mr Chung could stand it no longer. He picked up the microphone and delivered a few well-chosen words in his native tongue and hung up. There was a stunned silence, followed by "Was that you Dai?" "No. What was it Griff?" "Dunno, but it sounded like double Dutch to me boy!"

TINNING LINES. Still with S.C.W., I went to Velindre for three days which turned into three weeks. The tinning line took on steel strips and coated it electronically with tin in a continuous process. There were two pay-off reels so that when one reel expired the head of the second reel was welded to the tail of the first. This had to be done very quickly as it involved stopping the pay-off reels. To enable this to be done there were three looping pits each 80 feet deep. While the strip was being joined the rest of the line continued at reduced speed using up the strip from the pits. The first time the crew tried to make a join they were not quick enough and the whole line ground to a noisy halt. Our friend Mr. Chung came dashing down into the basement where most of the Witton detachment were gathered. "Come on you lot" he shouted, "Get your shovels and into the pit. They want another 40 feet!"

In order to keep the pits full of strip it was necessary to have photo-electric monitors to check the lengths of the hanging loops. The monitors were not working as they should so someone had to enter one of the pits and bring out one (or more) of the units for checking. On the bench all was well so back it went. It still failed in the pit. History does not relate how many times those units went up and down before someone twigged the explanation. The circuits controlled by the contacts of the p-e units were ac powered but the contacts were bench-checked by a dc continuity meter. There were spark-suppression capacitors across the contacts of the p-e units which passed enough current to operate the ac circuits whether the contacts were open or closed.

ELECTRONIC SECTION, RECTIFIER WORKS. When I joined the Section the "egg-head" (to quote a phrase not then in use) who had most of the ideas was the one and only Sam Dale. Apart from Electrical Engineering he could speak at length about Fishing, Photography, Pronunciation of Welsh names, Cars, and Motorbikes and he used to make and play violins as well. We all learned a lot from Sam. He once had an exciting contest with one of the outside photographers (was it Whybrow?). Sam had a beautiful polished wooden quarter-plate camera and he would say "I have got a swing head on my camera". Mr. Whybrow would come back with "Oh yes Mr. Dale but I have a flying widget on mine". This seemed to go for minutes and we were all flapping our ears because we had never heard Sam under such heavy pressure.

Because of some injury Sam was unable to apply pressure to one of the violin strings, but he got over this by wrapping several turns of a rubber band round the bent finger. He had the necessary tendons to lift the finger from the string and the rubber band pulled it down again when he relaxed the finger. One Christmas he was playing some carols which involved all sorts of facial contortions which some of us found slightly embarrassing. While he was in full swing, Percy Reeves came in from Rectifier Test and in his blunt way he said "What are you pulling funny faces for Sam?".

Sam was always turning up with another old car. He went through several Rileys but the one I remember best was a Citroen Light 15.

That is the one that Maigret used to drive on T/V. He took me once to Quinton where I then lived, and I knew all the road defects on the way. As we approached one nasty pot-hole I tensed myself as usual but there was no bang and I had to admire the suspension as we floated on in comfort.

Sam was most meticulous in over-hauling the mechanical side of his vehicles. On the Rileys the brakes were cable operated and there was a complex system of pulleys to balance the brakes, all the pulleys being on ball-bearing rings. Of course all the bearings were full of ancient grease so he had to strip them, clean and re-pack them to get the brakes to work to his satisfaction. One day Ken Birks, the Works Manager came in as we were getting an update on the car situation. After listening Ken spoke the immortal phrase, "The day will come Sam, when you will realise that there are other things in life apart from lying under oily cars".

Sam used to spend his summer holidays fishing in the North of Scotland. He always took his elderly mother and she stayed in the hotel while he visited lonely lochs each day. We always got a blow-by-blow account of the journeys (this was long before the advent of motorways) and we became familiar with Tyndrum, Creanlarich, Stac Pollaidh and Achilyibuie. I found it quite exciting when my wife and I started to visit Scotland in the 80's and came upon these names. We thought "Old Sammy set foot here 35 years ago!"

Jim Benson was another Character in MAR. When asked by an Ape "Have you got a rule Jim?" his answer was "Yes—Never lend tools to apprentices". He had a special steel rule which he used to lend to people who made a nuisance of themselves. While using the "gullenteen" (local pronunciation) in the Lab he was careless enough to get his steel rule in the way of the blade. Being an economical guy he trimmed the end so that it began at 1 instead of 0. The uninitiated found that anything made using the Benson rule came out under-sized, and they usually didn't notice until it was nearly finished.

Jim used to have his lunch at the Magnet Club with Jimmy Welford and others. JB was complaining about the quality of the rice pudding which was even stiffer than usual. He said it was so stiff that he could invert the plate and it would not fall off, and he tried to demonstrate this. He took the plate with one hand each side, lifted it up and rotated it about the horizontal axis. Unfortunately the pudding left the plate and the rotation spun it across the table where it landed on JW's gauntlets. At any rate that's how it was told to me.

LOUDON PLANER. Shortly before I went into MAR the Electronics Section produced a reversing drive for a new Loudon Planer in Big Shop. It was powered by the smallest grid controlled tank that we made. Controlling one of these beasts is not just like controlling a high-vacuum valve (Remember them?)

The grids required a good kick to trigger them off so you have a square-wave transformer which sits at the output of a phase-shifting network. Advance the phase, and the output of the tank goes up. So far so good, when you want to reverse the direction of the motor it gets more complicated, and that's where the trouble can be expected. The story goes that while the system was being tested in MAR the motor "stamped its foot". In other words there was a failure to control the output of the tank when it should have been in inversion mode and there was a dramatic over-current in the motor armature. The controls include a typical PO relay, and it was surmised that a floating seed of willow herb had got between the contacts at the worst possible moment!

When it was finally commissioned it gave good service apart from occasional hiccups Eventually, it was decided that the margins were a little tight and the next size of tank was installed. It did not fit in the cubicle of course, but as it was mounted up in the girders, that did not matter.

EXCITEMENT AT HEAD WRIGHTSON. We had an order to put variable speed drives on some draw-benches that Head Wrightson were supplying to IMI, if I remember aright. I had to go up to Middlesbrough with Ray Judd to assist with the commissioning. These massive draw-benches took 3 tubes which were rammed into the dies, far enough for the ends to be gripped by clamps on the traveller. This traveller, a large complicated unit was banged up against the die block by a steel cable hard *enough* to cause the clamps(*on the traveller*) to grip the tubes (*so that the traveller could then draw out the tubes through the dies for the length of the bench to form the final sized tubes required*).

The main drive consisted of a very substantial chain which was driven at idling speed from (guess what?) a steel tank rectifier. Once the tubes were in the clamps, a mighty hook which was pivoted on the traveller, dropped into engagement with the chain and the main motor was accelerated, taking hook, traveller, and tubes down the draw-bench. Since the die blocks were fixed, the tubes were dragged through the dies. When the tail end of the tubes dropped out of the dies the motor load dropped substantially and the hook was supposed to (*automatically*) pull out of the chain links. Of course there were some ramps at the bottom end of the bench to force the hook out of the chain if it lingered.

On one run the hook did not dis-engage and someone was just about to press the emergency stop button when someone else said "we might as well check the last-ditch" and so it was allowed to run on. Well the ramps pushed the hook up but it did not un-hook the chain. That traveller must have weighed 10-20 tons but it looped up in the air where the chain passed over the pulley and crashed down between the bench and all our lovely panels and finished up on the heap of inter-connecting wires and chopped them up. Fortunately no-one was hurt but from where I was standing at the other side of the panels, I saw them pivoting forward towards me but they did not keep coming. It turned out that someone had got the wrong profile on the hook and it was undercut too much.

PANIC IN TRANSFORMER WORKS. I had a front seat view of a crane accident when they were lifting a big CEGB transformer. It is a very labour intensive job to assemble the laminations, then turn the core to stand up, after which you take out the top limb bit by bit, ready to lower the coils on to the vertical limbs. All this is done with scaffolds around the beast. Then you have to re-assemble the top limb. Then, and then only, you take it to the ovens. Now this should be a straight lift out of the nest of scaffolding, but it was such a monster that it was going to take 3 cranes to do the lift.

One crane was hitched to the South end of the transformer while the other 2 cranes were shackled to the ends of a lifting beam, the centre of which was attached to the North end of the transformer. They had got it almost clear of the scaffolding when crane 1 (North) was seen to be in difficulties. I think he was trying to stop his crane but maybe the brake was slipping—at any rate his hook began to descend, which left the other two in a quandary. The only thing was to lower the other two cranes to keep everything level but the beam was now out of the horizontal and the transformer was not horizontal so when it entered the scaffolding the corner hit the scaffold poles and it canted right over before it came to rest.

There was a pause of about 5 minutes while the Witton Bush Telegraph got into action then people began to pour in to look at the wreckage. I should have made a charge for describing what happened but it never occurred to me. Fool!

When they re-built it, weeks later, they had three men on each crane for the next lift which was quite uneventful in spite of all those watchers.

EARLY DAYS. We did not always employ the mighty steel tank rectifiers for our drives for small motors. We did some equipment powered by Thyratrons, which were glass "bottles" containing an anode, a cathode, a grid and a small quantity of mercury vapour. When the grid was driven positive w.r.t. the cathode, the gas would be ionised allowing conduction to the anode which was supplied by ac. It all provided a controllable voltage to the motor. We were asked to make a treversible drive for a lathe using this sort of system. They sent us a drawing of their lathe and said "Can you fit it in that enclosure?" We had to write back and say "No but we can get your lathe in our control panel, but what shall we do with the operator?"

It was a pity as it did all they wanted—-3000 rpm forward to 3000 rpm reverse in 6 seconds for screw-cutting in brass. They installed it in their development dept up against a partition and hid our cubicle behind the partition.

PRACTICAL JOKERS. In the Electronic Section we went through a spell of foolish pranks. One recalls one office desk which banked up against a wall. The handles of the drawers were un-screwed, the desk was turned round and replaced against the wall. Fake drawers were drawn in with blue crayon and the handles were re-fitted. It looked just as before and the occupant sat down and got on with his work. All eyes were hanging out awaiting the moment when he would want something out of his drawer. Foolish happy days. I never minded coming back off holiday.

JUST ONE MORE. Just a word about Ron Bates the Great Traveller. He used to travel daily from Stourbridge (*30 miles?*) to Witton and back. He did it by train and he did it on a series of cars and vans such as Bradfords (Jowetts) and old Rileys. He took his wife off to Spain on their honeymoon in something totally unsuitable which broke down before he got to the ferry. He nursed it back home, spent about a week repairing it and set out again. He had a head-on collision with an Austin Ruby which resulted in a write-off. Ron purchased the remains at scrap price and set about straightening out the frame. He used to borrow clamps and such-like from Witton and take them home in his brief-case He made such a good job that he took out some bends that were meant to be there, and had to re-introduce them. I cannot remember if he had it on the road again but I like to think that he did.

When the great amalgam took place he had to start working at Rugby, but he still lived in Stourbridge.

APPENDIX 3.

The gambling demonstration

"It's a lovely little toy," explained the deputy to Roger some days later. "When you press this button at the front, one of the two lamps will light up and stay lit showing either 'heads' or 'tails. That is quite a random choice, as when you touch this button, the electronics pick out the first half cycle of the incoming mains supply, and if it is the positive half cycle, it selects the 'heads', and if it is the negative half cycle it selects 'tails'. That lights one of the display lights. As the mains supply is at fifty cycles per second, it is obviously a random choice of which is selected each time you touch the button."

"I see that" said Roger slowly, "but what does that prove?"

"Now the mathematics come in," continued the deputy, "What is the chance of your first throw being a 'head'?"

"Well, fifty-fifty of course," replied Roger.

"Correct," said the deputy," or expressed mathematically, the odds are 1 in 2, OK?"

"Carry on," said Roger. "Now," continued the deputy "if you do a second touch of the button you will by now have had four alternative sequences, the alternatives before of H or T will now be HH, HT, TH, or TT agreed?"

"Yes," said Roger listening carefully, the deputy was sketching this out on a piece of paper as he spoke.

"Thus," he continued, "the odds on getting either an HH or TT on this second throw is 1 in 4, and on each touch of the button, the number of alternative combinations for the sequence so far is doubled. The second throw gave the odds of 1 in 4, and the third throw gives odds 1 in 8. If you continue, it will be 1 in 16 at the fourth throw and so on. if you express this mathematically, you can say that if you take 'n' consecutive throws the chances of them all being heads or tails becomes '2 to the power of n.' For example, eight consecutive would give you 2 to the power of 8, that would be 1 chance in 128."

"I think I get it," said Roger. "It's a bit like the old single grain of wheat story on the first square of the chess board, if you then double up on each next square, you would end up on the sixty fourth square with more than all the wheat in the world."

"Exactly so," beamed the deputy "Now can you go off and explain this in a nice diagrammatic form to put up here as a display?

" "Right, I'll have a go," said Roger "it will be interesting to try." He thought for a minute. "But how does this device help?" He suddenly realised that he had agreed maths, but still had no idea how the device could prove it.

"Ah, that's the clever bit," said the deputy. "See those counters at the back? They are counting all the time, and if you press the button, say 50 times, one counter will tell you the number of tries you had, and the other counter will display the longest combination of consecutive 'heads' or 'tails' that occurred. If you don't believe the electronics, you can jot down on a piece of paper each 'head'" or 'tail' as it comes up and make your own notes. From all this, you can draw on a graph the number of tries you had against the number of consecutive runs. We tried it all day yesterday, and the more we did, the more the average curve came out to exactly the formula. That was quite uncanny, and absolutely proved the general formula ." He paused for effect, "and this is conclusive proof that however many consecutive heads or tails you get in a sequence, the odds on the next one are still 50/50!"

Roger found he had to agree the logic. "And do these electronic valves work all this out and do the counting?"

"Of course," said the deputy. "We are very keen on electronics here in the labs, we are certain they will have a big role in future engineering control systems, and we take every chance to try and interest the traditional engineers of their potential."

That night back at the Hall, Roger was still intrigued by the device, and tried himself by repeatedly throwing a dice, and calling the evens 'heads' and the odds 'tails' in order to simulate the doctor's device. He counted the number of tries to get three consecutive 'heads', and found after about 4 successes he had needed a total of 35 tries, which was an average of 8.25. "Crickey!" he exclaimed out loud, "almost exactly the mathematical answer of 8." Roger found himself very impressed. Two of his friends sitting near were startled when Roger spoke, they had been watching his doodling with the dice for some time.

"Are you alright?" they asked. "Or can we go and get you some pills?"

"No problem," laughed Roger, "I've been following up a numerical experiment we did in the lab today, and I feel like Archimedes when he shouted out 'Eureka' in the bath."

Roger sat down and sketched out exactly how the logic worked. "I've drawn up a chart," he said next day to the deputy head, "I spent all yesterday evening playing with ideas, and I actually tried out the theory by repeatedly throwing a dice."

"Good Heavens, you must be keen! did it work?"

"Yes, and it gave me this idea for a notice you could use at the next demonstration." Roger unrolled a sheet of paper with the following diagram on it;

A Demonstration
ODDS ON CONSECUTIVE HEADS OR TAILS

Try No:							ODDS
1		H	or		T		1:2
2	H	or	T	H	or	T	1:4
3	H or T	H or T	H or T	H or T			1:8
"n"		.... ETC.					$1:2^n$

(This experiment generates a genuine random "heads" or "tails" with every touch of the control button. With the aid of the counter, you can check the above pattern yourself. Every chance of another "head" increases the odds of an overall run of "heads" (or "tails") by a factor of 2, this proves conclusively, that even after any number of consecutive "heads"(say), the chance of the next touch being another "head" is still exactly 1:2 ie 50/50)

TO CHECK YOURSELF, START THE DEVICE BY SETTING THE COUNTER TO ZERO, AND REPEATEDLY TAP THE BUTTON UNTIL YOU ACHIEVE **THREE** SUCCESIVE "HEADS" OR "TAILS". THE COUNTER WILL TELL YOU THEN HOW MANY TRIES YOU NEEDED. PLACE YOUR NUMBER ON THE ATTACHED SHEET, AND YOU WILL SEE THAT THE **AVERAGE** NUMBER APPROACHES NEARER AND NEARER TO THE ABOVE THEORETICAL FIGURE OF **EIGHT !**

The Deputy studied the chart carefully, "I like this," he said. "Thank you very much, I'll get this printed up neatly in colours. I hope future visitors will understand it, it might even put some of them off gambling!" he added with a laugh. "The other evening, I found someone sitting here trying to reach ten consecutive heads or tails! He had been at it for some time, and I pointed out to him that the average number of tries he might need was over one thousand, and it could easily be double that before he got one." The deputy smiled and carried on. "We encourage keenness, but after the lad thought about it for a minute, he gave up and went home. Good job too! because then I could lock the place up and go home myself!"

THE AUTHOR

K. C. Parton, CE, FIEE, Bsc.(Hons), spent twenty-one years at GEC Witton, starting as a graduate apprentice and finishing as Manager of Technical Services, including the laboratories, and the introduction of on-site computing. During this time he had a number of technical papers published in the journal of the Institution of Electrical Engineers and became chairman of the IEE specialist committee G9 (Power System Stability and Operation). He also held a number of patents on Super-conducting Fault Limiters.

Outside of work, he was also prominent in apprentice activities including a period as editor of the quarterly apprentices Journal, and wrote a number of full length comic reviews for the annual apprentice's dinners.

After the rationalising of the industry during the 60s he became Managing Director of a GEC Computer Services company covering a wide area of allied manufacturing units in the Midlands. He subsequently moved into more managerial appointments, but never lost his love of shop-floor humour and the direct manufacturing industry.

The author is now retired and living in Broughton Hackett near Worcester. He is married with 4 children, and at the last count had eight grandchildren.